WORDLY WISE 3000™ Book 6

Test Booklet

SECOND EDITION

EDUCATORS PUBLISHING SERVICE
Cambridge and Toronto

Printed in USA

ISBN 978-0-8388-2936-3

6 7 8 9 10 MLY 14 13 12 11 10

Book 6, Lesson 1 Test

Find a SYNONYM for each underlined word. Then fill in the circle next to your answer.

1. He shows <u>affection</u> for his family.

   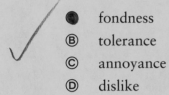

   - Ⓐ ● fondness
   - Ⓑ tolerance
   - Ⓒ annoyance
   - Ⓓ dislike

2. The speaker's <u>eloquence</u> impressed everyone in the audience.

   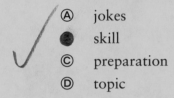

   - Ⓐ jokes
   - Ⓑ ● skill
   - Ⓒ preparation
   - Ⓓ topic

3. They <u>contributed</u> to the Red Cross.

   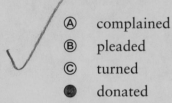

   - Ⓐ complained
   - Ⓑ pleaded
   - Ⓒ turned
   - Ⓓ ● donated

4. There is a new <u>exhibit</u> at the park headquarters.

   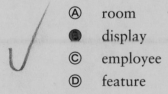

   - Ⓐ room
   - Ⓑ ● display
   - Ⓒ employee
   - Ⓓ feature

5. Young people often have <u>lofty</u> ideals.

   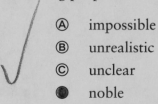

   - Ⓐ impossible
   - Ⓑ unrealistic
   - Ⓒ unclear
   - Ⓓ ● noble

1

6. Jennie <u>clasped</u> the puppy.

    Ⓐ calmed

    Ⓑ caught

    ● held

    Ⓓ claimed

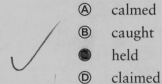

Find an ANTONYM for each underlined word. Then fill in the circle next to your answer.

7. The architect will <u>unveil</u> the plans for the new park.

    Ⓐ halt

    Ⓑ explain

    Ⓒ refuse

    ● conceal

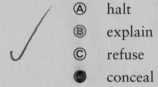

8. <u>Poverty</u> means different things in different countries.

    Ⓐ unkindness

    ● wealth

    Ⓒ crime

    Ⓓ economics

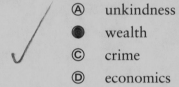

9. Haley has an <u>affectionate</u> nature.

    Ⓐ quiet

    Ⓑ meek

    ● cold

    Ⓓ sly

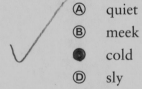

10. Dylan is an <u>eloquent</u> speaker.

    Ⓐ graceful

    Ⓑ forgetful

    Ⓒ intense

    ● clumsy

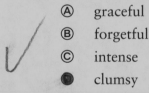

11. Ms. Allen received an <u>appeal</u> from the resource center.

    ● speech

    Ⓑ donation

    Ⓒ praise

    Ⓓ letter

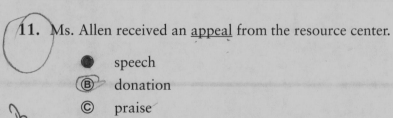

12. The red jacket made her <u>conspicuous</u>.

    Ⓐ   unnoticeable

    Ⓑ   uncomfortable

    Ⓒ   unattractive

    Ⓓ   unsure

Choose the BEST way to complete each sentence or answer each question. Then fill in the circle next to your answer.

13. The lawyer <u>appealed</u> for mercy. <u>Appealed</u> means

    Ⓐ   demanded.

    Ⓑ   gave reasons.

    Ⓒ   argued against.

    Ⓓ   asked.

14. Which is most likely to organize an <u>exhibition</u>?

    Ⓐ   a school committee

    Ⓑ   a group of paintings

    Ⓒ   the museum staff

    Ⓓ   a service station

15. Where is a <u>ferry</u> most likely to be found?

    Ⓐ   in a garden

    Ⓑ   at a dock

    Ⓒ   in a book

    Ⓓ   in the wilderness

16. Which of the following <u>contribute</u> to snowy weather?

    Ⓐ   high snow banks

    Ⓑ   cold temperatures

    Ⓒ   icicles on trees

    Ⓓ   closed roads

17. To <u>declare</u> that you believe something is to

    Ⓐ   insist that you don't believe it.

    Ⓑ   suggest that you might believe it.

    Ⓒ   make known that you believe it.

    Ⓓ   lie that you do believe it.

3

18. The speaker's <u>lofty</u> attitude made it clear that

    Ⓐ   she was well informed.

    Ⓑ   she was standing on a platform.

    Ⓒ   she believed in what she was saying.

    ●   she felt herself superior to her audience.

19. When Brian <u>exhibited</u> his knowledge, he

    ●   showed his knowledge in public.

    Ⓑ   made good use of his knowledge.

    Ⓒ   doubted his knowledge.

    Ⓓ   put on a show in a gallery.

20. To be <u>persecuted</u> is to be

    Ⓐ   arrested.

    Ⓑ   taken to court.

    ●   treated cruelly.

    Ⓓ   chased.

21. Which of the following might have a <u>clasp</u>?

    Ⓐ   a safe

    Ⓑ   a refrigerator door

    ●   a bracelet

    Ⓓ   a scarf

22. An <u>immigrant</u> is someone who

    Ⓐ   is leaving his or her homeland.

    Ⓑ   travels often to other countries.

    Ⓒ   travels in a wagon train.

    ●   is coming into a new country.

23. What do the <u>contributors</u> to a magazine do?

    Ⓐ   review the magazine

    ●   supply stories to be printed in the magazine

    Ⓒ   buy copies of the magazine

    Ⓓ   sell the magazine in their stores

4

24. The mayor is most likely to <u>unveil</u>

    Ⓐ   a new park.

    ●   a new law.

    ©   a new statue.

    Ⓓ   a new window.

25. A <u>pedestal</u> is most likely to hold

    Ⓐ   a small pig.

    Ⓑ   a feast.

    ©   a bicycle.

    ●   a vase.

26. The committee wrote a <u>declaration</u> of purpose. <u>Declaration</u> means

    Ⓐ   plan.

    ●   public statement.

    ©   description.

    Ⓓ   argument for.

27. Which is likely to hold the most <u>appeal</u> to a teacher?

    ●   a relaxed vacation

    Ⓑ   a shortage of textbooks

    ©   an extra course to teach

    Ⓓ   committee work

28. What could <u>ferry</u> two or three people?

    Ⓐ   an automobile

    Ⓑ   a helicopter

    ●   a rowboat

    Ⓓ   a buggy

29. Which can be <u>lofty</u>?

    Ⓐ   a bed

    Ⓑ   a cabin

    ©   a farm

    ●   mountains

30. The <u>persecution</u> of the family included

   Ⓐ sending them threatening notes.
   Ⓑ selling them magazine subscriptions.
   Ⓒ walking dogs past their house.
   Ⓓ taking over fresh-baked cookies.

31. I laughed at the baby's <u>clasp</u> on my finger. <u>Clasp</u> means

   Ⓐ ring.
   Ⓑ grip.
   Ⓒ bite.
   Ⓓ tug.

32. One way to make a <u>contribution</u> to a charity is to

   Ⓐ write to it.
   Ⓑ find out what its purpose is.
   Ⓒ send poor people to it.
   Ⓓ volunteer time working for it.

33. The book <u>appeals</u> to children. <u>Appeals</u> means

   Ⓐ bores.
   Ⓑ disgusts.
   Ⓒ interests.
   Ⓓ insults.

6

Book 6, Lesson 2 Test

Find a SYNONYM for each underlined word. Then fill in the circle next to your answer.

1. The company president was an <u>arrogant</u> person.

    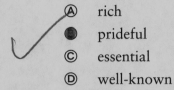

    - Ⓐ rich
    - Ⓑ prideful
    - Ⓒ essential
    - Ⓓ well-known

2. Thoughtless people <u>violate</u> the beauty of the wilderness.

    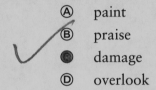

    - Ⓐ paint
    - Ⓑ praise
    - Ⓒ damage
    - Ⓓ overlook

3. Many cultures have <u>ceremonies</u> to celebrate birthdays.

    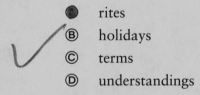

    - Ⓐ rites
    - Ⓑ holidays
    - Ⓒ terms
    - Ⓓ understandings

4. The baseball team gave a <u>triumphant</u> shout.

    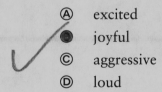

    - Ⓐ excited
    - Ⓑ joyful
    - Ⓒ aggressive
    - Ⓓ loud

5. <u>Integrate</u> what you know with what you are learning.

    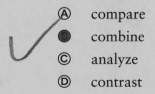

    - Ⓐ compare
    - Ⓑ combine
    - Ⓒ analyze
    - Ⓓ contrast

6. The police <u>detained</u> the suspect.

    Ⓐ   questioned

    Ⓑ   identified

    Ⓒ   pursued

    ●   held

Find an ANTONYM for each underlined word. Then fill in the circle next to your answer.

7. They are <u>vacating</u> their apartment.

    Ⓐ   decorating

    Ⓑ   leaving

    ●   occupying

    Ⓓ   selling

8. Getting caught shoplifting was a <u>degrading</u> experience.

    ●   uplifting

    Ⓑ   boring

    Ⓒ   forgettable

    Ⓓ   hilarious

9. Becoming an artist was a <u>supreme</u> goal of his life.

    Ⓐ   previous

    ●   minor

    Ⓒ   temporary

    Ⓓ   unexamined

10. Chelsea <u>violated</u> her promise.

    Ⓐ   broke

    Ⓑ   inflicted

    Ⓒ   suspended

    ●   kept

11. Camels seem to have a look of <u>arrogance</u>.

    Ⓐ   cheerfulness

    Ⓑ   liveliness

    ●   meekness

    Ⓓ   interest

Choose the BEST way to complete each sentence or answer each question. Then fill in the circle next to your answer.

12. The <u>campaign</u> for a new library is underway. <u>Campaign</u> describes

     Ⓐ   the construction of the building.

     Ⓑ   the design of the building.

     Ⓒ   the election of the director of the library.

     ●   planned efforts to get a new library.

13. Half of the class <u>boycotted</u> the event. This means that they

     Ⓐ   helped put on the event.

     Ⓑ   ridiculed the event.

     ●   refused to attend the event.

     Ⓓ   attended the event.

14. The speaker <u>extended</u> her hand to the company president after the speech. This means that she

     ●   held out her hand.

     Ⓑ   offered to help.

     Ⓒ   accepted an offer of help.

     Ⓓ   thanked the president for help.

15. Who might wear an expression of <u>triumph</u>?

     ●   the winner of a spelling bee

     Ⓑ   a diner in a restaurant

     Ⓒ   a criminal being sent to jail

     Ⓓ   someone in an earthquake

16. To have <u>custody</u> of someone is to

     ●   send the person to jail.

     Ⓑ   give part-time care to the person.

     Ⓒ   act as the person's guardian.

     Ⓓ   be related to that person.

17. Farragut led the <u>campaign</u> to seize New Orleans. This means that he

     Ⓐ   was trying to capture the most votes.

     ●   headed the military moves to capture the city.

     Ⓒ   was in charge of the plan to replace its mayor.

     Ⓓ   marched at the head of angry mob.

18. To <u>extend</u> human life would be to

   Ⓐ study it thoroughly.
   Ⓑ value it highly.
   Ⓒ understand it well.
   ● make it longer.

19. When can you expect a legal <u>verdict</u>?

   Ⓐ when you apply for a driver's license
   Ⓑ when you run a red light
   ● at the end of a trial
   Ⓓ when a lawyer is summing up a case

20. A <u>violation</u> of your civil rights is

   Ⓐ an explanation of the rights you have.
   Ⓑ an action that denies you your legal rights.
   Ⓒ a questioning of your rights.
   ● a temporary limitation of your rights.

21. When Octavian returned to Rome in <u>triumph</u>, he had just

   Ⓐ had a long rest on his country estate.
   Ⓑ come to ask for more money.
   ● conquered Rome's enemies.
   Ⓓ bought a new chariot.

22. The male lions had to be <u>segregated</u> so they did not fight. <u>Segregated</u> means

   Ⓐ fed often.
   Ⓑ drugged.
   ● kept apart.
   Ⓓ carefully introduced to one another.

23. The <u>supreme</u> representative of the American people is

   Ⓐ the average family.
   Ⓑ a court justice.
   Ⓒ a state senator.
   ● the president of the United States.

24. Who is most likely to take someone into <u>custody</u>?

    Ⓐ   a nurse

    Ⓑ   the manager of a bank

    Ⓒ   a police officer

    Ⓓ   a teacher

25. Joshua's aunt is <u>campaigning</u> for state senator. This means that she

    Ⓐ   is in the state senate.

    Ⓑ   is running for the office of state senator.

    Ⓒ   is employed by a state senator.

    Ⓓ   is writing speeches for a state senator.

26. Stephanie <u>degraded</u> herself by cheating on her math test. <u>Degraded</u> means

    Ⓐ   relieved.

    Ⓑ   disgraced.

    Ⓒ   upset.

    Ⓓ   exasperated.

27. Nathan suggested a <u>boycott</u> of non-union stores. In this case, a <u>boycott</u> is

    Ⓐ   a group decision to stop dealing with those stores.

    Ⓑ   a conference with the store managers.

    Ⓒ   a plan to identify these stores.

    Ⓓ   a plan to show support of these stores.

28. Spain's rule <u>extended</u> far to the north. <u>Extended</u> means

    Ⓐ   enlarged.

    Ⓑ   strengthened.

    Ⓒ   weakened.

    Ⓓ   stretched.

29. To give your <u>verdict</u> on something is to

    Ⓐ   give your word of honor.

    Ⓑ   state your opinion of it.

    Ⓒ   give a careful description of it.

    Ⓓ   commit yourself to doing it.

30. Integration is the process of

    Ⓐ   thinking about new ideas.

    Ⓑ   looking into something.

    ●   uniting different elements into a whole.

    Ⓓ   dividing something into parts.

31. To triumph over bad habits is to

    Ⓐ   worry about them.

    Ⓑ   win an argument about them.

    ©   attempt to break them.

    ●   overcome them.

32. What is an example of segregation?

    ●   putting students of different races in different schools

    Ⓑ   holding protest marches

    ©   making laws that defy the United States Constitution

    Ⓓ   putting students of different races in the same school

33. To extend an invitation to your neighbors is to

    Ⓐ   withdraw it.

    Ⓑ   carry it.

    ©   offer it.

    ●   forward it.

Book 6, Lesson 3 Test

Find a SYNONYM for each underlined word. Then fill in the circle next to your answer.

1. A <u>horde</u> of people waited outside the auditorium.

    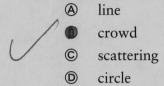
    - Ⓐ line
    - ● crowd
    - Ⓒ scattering
    - Ⓓ circle

2. The twins have <u>distinct</u> personalities.

    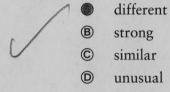
    - ● different
    - Ⓑ strong
    - Ⓒ similar
    - Ⓓ unusual

3. Allison's version of events is <u>incredible</u>.

    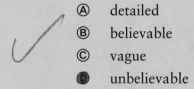
    - Ⓐ detailed
    - Ⓑ believable
    - Ⓒ vague
    - ● unbelievable

4. New England was a <u>sanctuary</u> to the Puritans.

    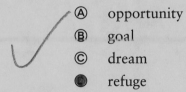
    - Ⓐ opportunity
    - Ⓑ goal
    - Ⓒ dream
    - ● refuge

5. Few people <u>inhabit</u> that region.

    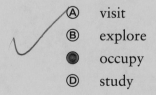
    - Ⓐ visit
    - Ⓑ explore
    - ● occupy
    - Ⓓ study

6. The book describes the <u>splendor</u> of ancient Rome.

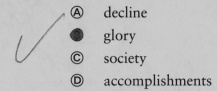

    Ⓐ decline
    Ⓑ glory
    © society
    Ⓓ accomplishments

Find an ANTONYM for each underlined word. Then fill in the circle next to your answer.

7. Not far from the palace, people lived in <u>squalor</u>.

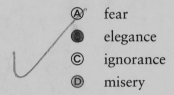

    Ⓐ fear
    Ⓑ elegance
    © ignorance
    Ⓓ misery

8. The <u>inhabitants</u> went to market on Saturdays.

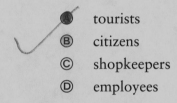

    Ⓐ tourists
    Ⓑ citizens
    © shopkeepers
    Ⓓ employees

9. Rain has been <u>abundant</u> these last two years.

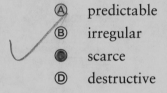

    Ⓐ predictable
    Ⓑ irregular
    © scarce
    Ⓓ destructive

10. Summer can be <u>humid</u> in the Southeast.

    Ⓐ rainy
    Ⓑ dry
    © cool
    Ⓓ sunny

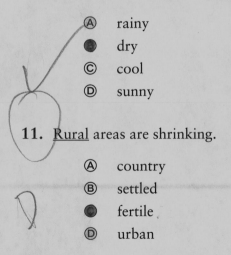

11. <u>Rural</u> areas are shrinking.

    Ⓐ country
    Ⓑ settled
    © fertile
    Ⓓ urban

12. Justin had a <u>hectic</u> school schedule.

   Ⓐ simple
   Ⓑ busy
   Ⓒ stressful
   Ⓓ confusing

Choose the BEST way to complete each sentence or answer each question. Then fill in the circle next to your answer.

13. The rock <u>grazed</u> the bear's shoulder. This means that the rock

   Ⓐ hit the bear with great force.
   Ⓑ barely scraped the bear as it went past.
   Ⓒ drew blood from the bear.
   Ⓓ sailed over the bear's shoulder without touching.

14. The three men crossed unfamiliar <u>terrain</u>. <u>Terrain</u> means

   Ⓐ a city grid.
   Ⓑ mountain ranges.
   Ⓒ trails.
   Ⓓ regions.

15. Which is most likely to have an <u>arid</u> climate?

   Ⓐ a sea coast
   Ⓑ a northern rainforest
   Ⓒ a desert
   Ⓓ a port town

16. If a country has an <u>abundance</u> of natural resources, it

   Ⓐ has more than one type of resource.
   Ⓑ has plenty of resources.
   Ⓒ has a shortage of resources.
   Ⓓ has unknown resources.

17. Which of the following has a <u>distinct</u> smell?

   Ⓐ fish
   Ⓑ water
   Ⓒ paper
   Ⓓ salt

18. The geese found <u>sanctuary</u> in the park. <u>Sanctuary</u> means

Ⓐ food.
Ⓑ nesting materials.
Ⓒ rivers and ponds.
Ⓓ protection.

19. Where is an animal most likely to <u>graze</u>?

Ⓐ in a dense forest
Ⓑ in a pasture
Ⓒ on top of a mountain
Ⓓ in a barn

20. A region's <u>terrain</u> is its

Ⓐ social history.
Ⓑ government.
Ⓒ surface features.
Ⓓ river system.

21. Which is most likely to appear <u>squalid</u>?

Ⓐ moldy cheese
Ⓑ a movie theater
Ⓒ a slum
Ⓓ a rain-soaked newspaper

22. The opera production was <u>splendid</u>. This means that it

Ⓐ lasted a long time.
Ⓑ inspired arguments.
Ⓒ took place in a huge theater.
Ⓓ impressed the audience.

23. The geographic opposite of a <u>peninsula</u> is

Ⓐ a river.
Ⓑ a deep inlet.
Ⓒ a pond.
Ⓓ an island.

24. The room most likely to have high <u>humidity</u> is

Ⓐ the bathroom.
Ⓑ the living room.
Ⓒ the bedroom.
Ⓓ the dining room.

16

Book 6, Lesson 4 Test

Find a SYNONYM for each underlined word. Then fill in the circle next to your answer.

1. The waves <u>buffeted</u> the cliff.

   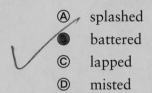
   Ⓐ splashed
   ● battered
   Ⓒ lapped
   Ⓓ misted

2. The meaning of the essay is <u>elusive</u>.

   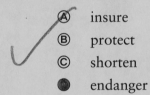
   Ⓐ deep
   Ⓑ shallow
   Ⓒ clear
   ● obscure

3. Firefighters may <u>jeopardize</u> their lives.

   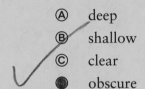
   Ⓐ insure
   Ⓑ protect
   Ⓒ shorten
   ● endanger

4. The boat was <u>moored</u> to the dock.

   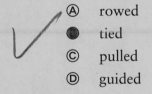
   Ⓐ rowed
   ● tied
   Ⓒ pulled
   Ⓓ guided

5. The ground ropes kept the hot-air balloon <u>stationary</u>.

   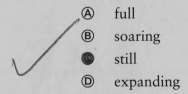
   Ⓐ full
   Ⓑ soaring
   ● still
   Ⓓ expanding

6. Mr. Mooney <u>swiveled</u> in his chair.

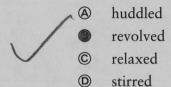

   Ⓐ huddled
   ● revolved
   © relaxed
   Ⓓ stirred

7. The bank robber <u>eluded</u> the guards.

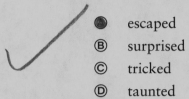

   ● escaped
   Ⓑ surprised
   © tricked
   Ⓓ taunted

Find an ANTONYM for each underlined word. Then fill in the circle next to your answer.

8. The wind <u>propelled</u> the sailboat.

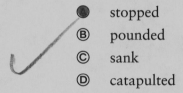

   ● stopped
   Ⓑ pounded
   © sank
   Ⓓ catapulted

9. The kite soon <u>plummeted</u>.

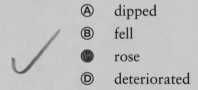

   Ⓐ dipped
   Ⓑ fell
   ● rose
   Ⓓ deteriorated

10. Some plants are more <u>flammable</u> than others.

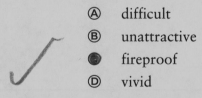

   Ⓐ difficult
   Ⓑ unattractive
   ● fireproof
   Ⓓ vivid

11. Kelsey did a <u>superb</u> job.

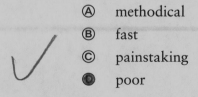

   Ⓐ methodical
   Ⓑ fast
   © painstaking
   ● poor

12. The economy has been <u>stationary</u> for the last two months.

    Ⓐ   unsatisfactory

    Ⓑ   thriving

    Ⓒ   unstable

    Ⓓ   unchanging

Choose the BEST way to complete each sentence or answer each question. Then fill in the circle next to your answer.

13. What would you find at a <u>buffet</u>?

    Ⓐ   a rocky shoreline

    Ⓑ   a long table with a variety of dishes on it

    Ⓒ   a menu

    Ⓓ   a large staff of waiters

14. Which of the following is a <u>mooring</u>?

    Ⓐ   a dock

    Ⓑ   a small boat

    Ⓒ   a length of rope

    Ⓓ   a sail

15. <u>Pollution</u> is to air as

    Ⓐ   butter is to milk.

    Ⓑ   wave is to ocean.

    Ⓒ   stain is to garment.

    Ⓓ   ice is to water.

16. Which of the following might have a <u>swivel</u>?

    Ⓐ   a bird's wing

    Ⓑ   a spray bottle

    Ⓒ   a trunk

    Ⓓ   the stand of a computer screen

17. Which of these things would you be likely to <u>inflate</u>?

    Ⓐ   a magazine

    Ⓑ   a baseball

    Ⓒ   a tire

    Ⓓ   a frog

18. Small mammals <u>attain</u> adulthood quickly. <u>Attain</u> means

    Ⓐ   pass through.

    Ⓑ   comprehend.

    Ⓒ   reach.

    Ⓓ   pursue.

19. One kind of <u>buffet</u> is

    Ⓐ   a piece of furniture for displaying dinnerware.

    Ⓑ   a strong breeze.

    Ⓒ   a collection of recipes.

    Ⓓ   a family celebration.

20. What <u>pollutes</u> the air?

    Ⓐ   mist

    Ⓑ   clouds

    Ⓒ   smoke

    Ⓓ   blizzards

21. Where might you be if you were <u>aloft</u>?

    Ⓐ   on a sled

    Ⓑ   in a plane

    Ⓒ   in a fast car

    Ⓓ   in a cabin

22. Caution is to <u>jeopardy</u> as

    Ⓐ   information is to knowledge.

    Ⓑ   safety is to education.

    Ⓒ   memory is to forgetfulness.

    Ⓓ   exercise is to poor health.

23. Which of the following can <u>hover</u>?

    Ⓐ   a rocket

    Ⓑ   a flying squirrel

    Ⓒ   a helicopter

    Ⓓ   a tennis ball

24. Panthers are <u>elusive</u> animals. This means that they are

    Ⓐ   aggressive.

    Ⓑ   hard to find or spot.

    Ⓒ   unstudied.

    Ⓓ   night hunters.

25. To <u>attain</u> something is to

    Ⓐ   achieve it.

    Ⓑ   catch it.

    Ⓒ   make good use of it.

    Ⓓ   understand it.

Book 6, Lesson 5 Test

Find a SYNONYM for each underlined word. Then fill in the circle next to your answer.

1. The monkey's <u>antics</u> entertained us.

   (A) expressions
   (B) feats
   (C) mischief
   (D) gestures

2. The stone's <u>inscription</u> was hard to make out.

   (A) purpose
   (B) structure
   (C) age
   (D) writing

3. His <u>attire</u> for the prom was expensive.

   (A) clothing
   (B) decoration
   (C) hairstyle
   (D) corsage

4. The children <u>stifled</u> their giggles.

   (A) finished
   (B) silenced
   (C) delayed
   (D) squealed

5. The old house was <u>shrouded</u> by fog.

   (A) misted
   (B) soaked
   (C) covered
   (D) dominated

6. The painting expresses a mood of <u>tranquility</u>.

    Ⓐ   calm

    Ⓑ   uneasiness

    Ⓒ   anger

    Ⓓ   despair

Find an ANTONYM for each underlined word. Then fill in the circle next to your answer.

7. The performance <u>captivated</u> everyone.

    Ⓐ   outlasted

    Ⓑ   interested

    Ⓒ   disgusted

    Ⓓ   attracted

8. The painters have been <u>diligent</u>.

    Ⓐ   creative

    Ⓑ   idle

    Ⓒ   active

    Ⓓ   unimaginative

9. Patrick has <u>deft</u> fingers.

    Ⓐ   long

    Ⓑ   quick

    Ⓒ   short

    Ⓓ   clumsy

10. They came up with a <u>tentative</u> solution.

    Ⓐ   disagreeable

    Ⓑ   approximate

    Ⓒ   definite

    Ⓓ   foolish

Choose the BEST way to complete each sentence or answer each question. Then fill in the circle next to your answer.

11. A <u>tranquil</u> scene might be

    Ⓐ   a storm at sea.

    Ⓑ   a blizzard blowing across the plains.

    Ⓒ   the rides at a fair.

    Ⓓ   a mountain lake on a sunny day.

12. A garment with <u>versatility</u> is

    Ⓐ   rainproof.

    Ⓑ   useful for many occasions.

    Ⓒ   worn over other garments.

    Ⓓ   made to last a long time.

13. Squirrels have an <u>innate</u> urge to store food. This means that squirrels

    Ⓐ   have a strong urge to bury nuts.

    Ⓑ   sometimes have the urge to store food.

    Ⓒ   know how to store food without being taught.

    Ⓓ   are trained by their parents to store food.

14. <u>Shrouds</u> are used to

    Ⓐ   cover dead bodies.

    Ⓑ   cover a bride's head during a wedding.

    Ⓒ   cover tables.

    Ⓓ   cover beds.

15. During a total <u>eclipse</u> of the sun, the sun

    Ⓐ   is visible from anywhere on earth.

    Ⓑ   blazes down upon the earth.

    Ⓒ   hides the moon from view.

    Ⓓ   is hidden by the moon.

16. They acted under the <u>shroud</u> of darkness. <u>Shroud</u> means

    Ⓐ   cover.

    Ⓑ   protection.

    Ⓒ   mist.

    Ⓓ   threat.

17. The novel <u>evolved</u> in the 1700s. This means that it

    Ⓐ   was like modern novels right from the first.

    Ⓑ   slowly developed and changed during the 1700s.

    Ⓒ   disappeared in the 1700s due to lack of interest.

    Ⓓ   declined in the 1700s and was not revived for a while.

18. To improve your <u>posture</u>, you should

    Ⓐ   study longer hours.

    Ⓑ   spend more time practicing.

    Ⓒ   sit up straight.

    Ⓓ   cut junk foods out of your diet.

19. What might <u>stifle</u> someone?

    Ⓐ   a hilarious remark

    Ⓑ   a solemn occasion

    Ⓒ   tiring work

    Ⓓ   poisonous gases

20. A <u>versatile</u> writer might produce

    Ⓐ   grim poetry.

    Ⓑ   essays, novels, and poetry.

    Ⓒ   one novel every five years.

    Ⓓ   two novels a year.

21. Which of the following is most likely to be <u>inscribed</u>?

    Ⓐ   a wedding ring

    Ⓑ   tissue paper

    Ⓒ   crayons

    Ⓓ   a newspaper

22. The director <u>attired</u> the actors appropriately. <u>Attired</u> means

    Ⓐ   gazed at.

    Ⓑ   criticized.

    Ⓒ   dressed.

    Ⓓ   scrubbed.

23. Does Mark Twain's writing <u>eclipse</u> Louisa May Alcott's? <u>Eclipse</u> means

    Ⓐ   seem like.

    Ⓑ   outdo.

    Ⓒ   influence.

    Ⓓ   mimic.

24. They <u>postured</u> as wealthy people. This means that they

    Ⓐ   were naturally arrogant.

    Ⓑ   had become rich late in life.

    Ⓒ   weren't wealthy but pretended to be.

    Ⓓ   posed for a lot of pictures.

25. <u>Evolution</u> is

    Ⓐ   the study of the earth's history.

    Ⓑ   the study of the movement of the planets.

    Ⓒ   a sudden change of present conditions.

    Ⓓ   the long, slow process of change.

Book 6, Lesson 6 Test

Find a SYNONYM for each underlined word. Then fill in the circle next to your answer.

1. The shop sells only the most expensive <u>apparel</u>.

   Ⓐ equipment

   Ⓑ supplies

   Ⓒ clothing

   Ⓓ furniture

2. As the rain let up, the sun <u>emerged</u>.

   Ⓐ blurred

   Ⓑ appeared

   Ⓒ set

   Ⓓ disappeared

3. What is the <u>function</u> of that machine?

   Ⓐ purpose

   Ⓑ origin

   Ⓒ cost

   Ⓓ speed

4. Everyone was in favor of Jordan's <u>motion</u>.

   Ⓐ signal

   Ⓑ activity

   Ⓒ proposal

   Ⓓ election

5. This chemical <u>inhibits</u> the growth of mold.

   Ⓐ feeds

   Ⓑ allows

   Ⓒ encourages

   Ⓓ discourages

6. The snow <u>dissolved</u> in the sunlight.

    Ⓐ glittered

    Ⓑ darkened

    Ⓒ froze

    Ⓓ melted

Find an ANTONYM for each underlined word. Then fill in the circle next to your answer.

7. The squirrel was <u>motionless</u> on the branch.

    Ⓐ sitting

    Ⓑ scampering

    Ⓒ unmoving

    Ⓓ sleeping

8. <u>Domesticated</u> elephants are common in India.

    Ⓐ trained

    Ⓑ loyal

    Ⓒ wild

    Ⓓ meek

9. The rain was <u>continuous</u> during March.

    Ⓐ unceasing

    Ⓑ steady

    Ⓒ welcome

    Ⓓ irregular

10. This jacket <u>sheds</u> water.

    Ⓐ discards

    Ⓑ absorbs

    Ⓒ defies

    Ⓓ oozes

11. A <u>minute</u> diamond was set in the ring.

    Ⓐ gigantic

    Ⓑ dull

    Ⓒ ordinary

    Ⓓ rough

12. Matthew is <u>inhibited</u> in new situations.

    Ⓐ   forgetful

    Ⓑ   remote

    Ⓒ   confident

    Ⓓ   desperate

13. The value of this painting has <u>appreciated</u>.

    Ⓐ   increased

    Ⓑ   retained

    Ⓒ   transformed

    Ⓓ   declined

Choose the BEST way to complete each sentence or answer each question. Then fill in the circle next to your answer.

14. To <u>hatch</u> a plan is to

    Ⓐ   oppose it.

    Ⓑ   come up with it.

    Ⓒ   examine it.

    Ⓓ   criticize it.

15. Which of the following is a <u>fiber</u>?

    Ⓐ   glue

    Ⓑ   fish scales

    Ⓒ   silk

    Ⓓ   flower petals

16. What can a <u>transfer</u> be used for?

    Ⓐ   to keep track of the time

    Ⓑ   to book a seat on an airplane

    Ⓒ   to get into a museum

    Ⓓ   to change from one bus to another

17. That bench can <u>function</u> as a storage unit. This means that

    Ⓐ   it has more than one use.

    Ⓑ   you should not sit on it.

    Ⓒ   it can only be used for storage.

    Ⓓ   it is part of a two-piece set.

18. Erica <u>motioned</u> to us to come in. <u>Motioned</u> means

    Ⓐ whispered.

    Ⓑ said in a loud voice.

    Ⓒ gave a hand signal.

    Ⓓ permitted.

19. Which of the following might be <u>shed</u> on something?

    Ⓐ liquid

    Ⓑ light

    Ⓒ clouds

    Ⓓ gases

20. Austin asked his company for a <u>transfer</u> to Oregon. He requested

    Ⓐ a new job there.

    Ⓑ a special phone line.

    Ⓒ a shipping order.

    Ⓓ a plane ticket.

21. What might someone do with a <u>hatch</u>?

    Ⓐ cook it

    Ⓑ live under it

    Ⓒ climb through it

    Ⓓ feed animals with it

22. Humans have <u>fibers</u> in their

    Ⓐ bones.

    Ⓑ muscles.

    Ⓒ fingernails.

    Ⓓ blood.

23. To <u>dissolve</u> a company is to

    Ⓐ break it up and shut it down.

    Ⓑ fund it.

    Ⓒ reorganize it.

    Ⓓ start it up.

24. To <u>shed</u> tears is to

    Ⓐ   conquer tears.

    Ⓑ   make fun of crying.

    Ⓒ   hold back tears.

    Ⓓ   let tears flow.

25. Native Americans <u>domesticated</u> corn. This means that they

    Ⓐ   used corn in many dishes.

    Ⓑ   exported corn to all parts of the Americas.

    Ⓒ   discovered that wild corn was edible.

    Ⓓ   turned wild corn into a cultivated plant.

26. Lindsay <u>appreciates</u> good Mexican food. This means that she

    Ⓐ   knows how to cook it.

    Ⓑ   introduces other people to it.

    Ⓒ   takes pleasure in its excellence.

    Ⓓ   collects Mexican recipes.

27. The mummy was <u>sheathed</u> in linen. This means that it

    Ⓐ   was dressed in elegant attire.

    Ⓑ   was given a protective linen wrapper.

    Ⓒ   was perfumed by linen.

    Ⓓ   was soaked in a linen liquid.

28. We saw <u>motion</u> in the bushes. This means that

    Ⓐ   the bushes stirred.

    Ⓑ   the seasons were changing.

    Ⓒ   we watched their growth over time.

    Ⓓ   the bushes were wet from the rain.

29. A college <u>function</u> might be

    Ⓐ   a required math class.

    Ⓑ   the person who heads the college.

    Ⓒ   a formal banquet for professors.

    Ⓓ   the college newspaper.

30. A student is likely to <u>transfer</u> after

      Ⓐ   studying all night for a test.

      Ⓑ   getting a poor grade in one subject.

      Ⓒ   passing notes in class.

      Ⓓ   moving into a new school district.

31. People <u>shed</u> skin cells. This means that we

      Ⓐ   are always growing new cells.

      Ⓑ   cast off dry skin cells.

      Ⓒ   cannot live without skin cells.

      Ⓓ   damage our skin cells.

32. Which of the following is true about <u>fiber</u> in foods?

      Ⓐ   It helps one's muscles grow stronger.

      Ⓑ   It provides necessary vitamins.

      Ⓒ   It is not digested.

      Ⓓ   It is bad for our bodies.

33. Which of the following is <u>hatched</u>?

      Ⓐ   a cottage

      Ⓑ   a puppy

      Ⓒ   a ship

      Ⓓ   a duckling

34. Shocking facts about the war are <u>emerging</u>. <u>Emerging</u> means

      Ⓐ   becoming known.

      Ⓑ   entertaining.

      Ⓒ   puzzling.

      Ⓓ   disturbing.

Book 6, Lesson 7 Test

Find a SYNONYM for each underlined word. Then fill in the circle next to your answer.

1. Mikayla <u>excels</u> at math.

   Ⓐ falters
   Ⓑ fails
   Ⓒ shines
   Ⓓ tutors

2. The doctor soon <u>soothed</u> the child.

   Ⓐ bandaged
   Ⓑ calmed
   Ⓒ silenced
   Ⓓ treated

3. <u>Hardy</u> sailors were needed for the voyage.

   Ⓐ tough
   Ⓑ unmarried
   Ⓒ experienced
   Ⓓ versatile

4. Where is the <u>origin</u> of the Nile River?

   Ⓐ outlet
   Ⓑ route
   Ⓒ port
   Ⓓ beginning

5. The puppets were <u>realistic</u>.

   Ⓐ attractive
   Ⓑ alive
   Ⓒ remarkable
   Ⓓ lifelike

6. The <u>monotony</u> of winter weather can be depressing.

Ⓒ glory

Ⓓ sameness

Ⓔ foolishness

Ⓕ heat

Find an ANTONYM for each underlined word. Then fill in the circle next to your answer.

7. His songs were all <u>mediocre</u>.

Ⓒ bland

Ⓓ solemn

Ⓔ outstanding

Ⓕ ordinary

8. The performance <u>exhausted</u> them.

Ⓒ revived

Ⓓ tired

Ⓔ irked

Ⓕ embarrassed

9. The baby needed <u>constant</u> attention.

Ⓒ aggressive

Ⓓ impatient

Ⓔ loving

Ⓕ occasional

10. After swimming, Christina was <u>ravenous</u>.

Ⓒ relaxed

Ⓓ full

Ⓔ dry

Ⓕ lively

11. People were asked to wear <u>casual</u> clothes to the party.

Ⓒ unsuccessful

Ⓓ formal

Ⓔ colorful

Ⓕ immense

12. Mr. Soo is a <u>veteran</u> photographer.

    Ⓐ   peaceful

    Ⓑ   unknown

    Ⓒ   beginning

    Ⓓ   natural

Choose the BEST way to complete each sentence or answer each question. Then fill in the circle next to your answer.

13. The two students <u>brawled</u> on the front lawn. <u>Brawled</u> means

    Ⓐ   sang loudly.

    Ⓑ   shouted insults at others.

    Ⓒ   had a picnic.

    Ⓓ   got into a fight.

14. We had a <u>casual</u> discussion about the problem. <u>Casual</u> means

    Ⓐ   unplanned.

    Ⓑ   calm.

    Ⓒ   animated.

    Ⓓ   hostile.

15. Their friends were <u>constant</u> throughout the crisis. <u>Constant</u> means

    Ⓐ   ready to give advice.

    Ⓑ   disloyal.

    Ⓒ   faithful.

    Ⓓ   unbiased.

16. The Clarks have <u>exhausted</u> their savings. This means that they

    Ⓐ   added to their savings.

    Ⓑ   have invested their savings.

    Ⓒ   are tired of saving money.

    Ⓓ   have used up all that they saved.

17. Early bargain-hunters <u>stampeded</u> through the shop doors. The shoppers

    Ⓐ   brought their pets into the store.

    Ⓑ   rushed inside in a wild group.

    Ⓒ   entered in a line.

    Ⓓ   stomped their feet as they entered.

18. An example of <u>punctuation</u> is

    Ⓐ   a flat tire.

    Ⓑ   a prompt answer.

    Ⓒ   a comma.

    Ⓓ   a wound.

19. My grandfather is called a <u>veteran</u> because he

    Ⓐ   gives health care to animals.

    Ⓑ   is quite old.

    Ⓒ   fought in the Korean War.

    Ⓓ   has had an adventurous life.

20. A person who is <u>realistic</u> is likely to

    Ⓐ   expect the worst.

    Ⓑ   never make plans.

    Ⓒ   look lifelike.

    Ⓓ   consider the cost of things.

21. He lost his jacket during the <u>brawl</u>. This means he lost it

    Ⓐ   during a heavy storm.

    Ⓑ   while he was fighting.

    Ⓒ   while moving in a crowd.

    Ⓓ   while chasing his dog.

22. I have a <u>casual</u> job babysitting for the Garcias. This means that I

    Ⓐ   babysit for them once in a while.

    Ⓑ   babysit for them every weekend.

    Ⓒ   don't dress up when I go to their house.

    Ⓓ   don't play with the children while I'm working.

23. A speaker might <u>punctuate</u> her remarks with

    Ⓐ   long words.

    Ⓑ   breathing.

    Ⓒ   gestures.

    Ⓓ   an entertaining style.

24. Which activity would be the most <u>monotonous</u>?

   Ⓐ   playing soccer

   Ⓑ   watching an adventure movie

   Ⓒ   watching a dryer go around

   Ⓓ   eating in a restaurant

25. The place where the race <u>originated</u> is

   Ⓐ   the place you send your registration form.

   Ⓑ   the city where the race takes place.

   Ⓒ   the finish line.

   Ⓓ   the starting point.

26. The aloe plant may <u>soothe</u> burns. This means that it

   Ⓐ   makes burns sting more.

   Ⓑ   may make the burns less painful.

   Ⓒ   often causes burns.

   Ⓓ   may make the burns heal more slowly.

27. To be <u>ravenous</u> for adventure is to

   Ⓐ   be terrified of taking risks.

   Ⓑ   be celebrated as an adventurer.

   Ⓒ   long intensely for adventure.

   Ⓓ   be paid for taking risks.

28. When it comes to acting, Adam is a <u>veteran</u>. This means he

   Ⓐ   is very experienced.

   Ⓑ   is very reliable.

   Ⓒ   likes to play young men.

   Ⓓ   plays the part of a soldier.

29. Pay attention when you <u>punctuate</u>

   Ⓐ   a cut on your finger.

   Ⓑ   an essay.

   Ⓒ   dinner at someone's house.

   Ⓓ   a movie.

30. Cowhands stay alert for <u>stampedes</u>. A <u>stampede</u> is

    Ⓐ   a wild animal that preys on cattle.

    Ⓑ   a mad dash of frightened animals.

    Ⓒ   a place where cattle can be pastured.

    Ⓓ   a cattle disease.

31. The law limits automobile <u>exhaust</u>. <u>Exhaust</u> refers to

    Ⓐ   the speed at which a car is driven.

    Ⓑ   the types of gasoline sold at stations.

    Ⓒ   engine power.

    Ⓓ   the waste gases from a car.

32. The <u>constant</u> temperature in the greenhouse helped the plants to grow. <u>Constant</u> means

    Ⓐ   unchanging.

    Ⓑ   varying.

    Ⓒ   high.

    Ⓓ   moderate.

Book 6, Lesson 8 Test

Find a SYNONYM for each underlined word. Then fill in the circle next to your answer.

1. Kelsey was <u>ecstatic</u> when she heard the news.

   Ⓐ depressed
   Ⓑ worried
   Ⓒ jubilant
   Ⓓ stunned

2. The <u>expedition</u> took them to Africa and Asia.

   Ⓐ journey
   Ⓑ airplane
   Ⓒ boat
   Ⓓ guide

3. The remote control is in a <u>convenient</u> spot.

   Ⓐ useless
   Ⓑ forgotten
   Ⓒ permanent
   Ⓓ handy

4. A <u>skirmish</u> was underway in the rats' cage.

   Ⓐ squall
   Ⓑ feast
   Ⓒ fight
   Ⓓ chase

5. It didn't take long for her to <u>retrieve</u> her bracelet.

   Ⓐ design
   Ⓑ recover
   Ⓒ purchase
   Ⓓ return

6. Ahead of us lay the grizzly bears' <u>territory</u>.

    Ⓐ relatives

    Ⓑ threats

    Ⓒ trails

    Ⓓ terrain

Find an ANTONYM for each underlined word. Then fill in the circle next to your answer.

7. Summer seemed to <u>linger</u> later this year.

    Ⓐ appear

    Ⓑ flee

    Ⓒ shrink

    Ⓓ resume

8. Devin was an <u>inept</u> painter.

    Ⓐ careless

    Ⓑ old-fashioned

    Ⓒ deft

    Ⓓ dull

9. The <u>captive</u> bird refused to sing.

    Ⓐ well-fed

    Ⓑ healthy

    Ⓒ happy

    Ⓓ liberated

10. Victoria's advice was <u>invaluable</u>.

    Ⓐ useless

    Ⓑ helpful

    Ⓒ wrong

    Ⓓ foolish

11. Ladybugs are <u>beneficial</u> in gardens.

    Ⓐ uncommon

    Ⓑ harmful

    Ⓒ popular

    Ⓓ helpful

12. The professor <u>interpreted</u> the formula for the class.

    Ⓐ   spoke

    Ⓑ   revised

    Ⓒ   obscured

    Ⓓ   explained

Choose the BEST way to complete each sentence or answer each question. Then fill in the circle next to your answer.

13. Ms. Bates <u>interpreted</u> the speech for the audience. <u>Interpreted</u> means

    Ⓐ   gave the speech in another language.

    Ⓑ   read the speech word for word.

    Ⓒ   presented a summary of the speech.

    Ⓓ   handed out copies of the speech.

14. Who is most likely to <u>accompany</u> a violinist?

    Ⓐ   a theater manager

    Ⓑ   a family member

    Ⓒ   a piano player

    Ⓓ   a member of the audience

15. A <u>supplement</u> to a dictionary is most likely to

    Ⓐ   be an all-new edition.

    Ⓑ   contain more words than the original.

    Ⓒ   explain how to use the dictionary.

    Ⓓ   contain words left out of the original.

16. <u>Captive</u> is to prison as

    Ⓐ   ring is to jewel box.

    Ⓑ   guard is to jail.

    Ⓒ   cage is to pen.

    Ⓓ   dictator is to country.

17. What would be a <u>convenience</u> in an apartment?

    Ⓐ   the apartment manager

    Ⓑ   a washing machine

    Ⓒ   noisy neighbors

    Ⓓ   carpet

18. The catnip put Snowball in a state of <u>ecstasy</u>. <u>Ecstasy</u> means

  Ⓐ unconsciousness.

  Ⓑ sickness.

  Ⓒ extreme happiness.

  Ⓓ confusion.

19. The <u>expedition</u> assembled in Cairo. <u>Expedition</u> means

  Ⓐ a collection of supplies for a journey.

  Ⓑ transportation for a long trip.

  Ⓒ a site where travelers camp.

  Ⓓ a group of explorers or soldiers.

20. Which of the following would be called an <u>expanse</u>?

  Ⓐ a flower garden

  Ⓑ a drought

  Ⓒ the surface of the ocean

  Ⓓ a skyscraper

21. An <u>inept</u> compliment is likely to

  Ⓐ thrill the recipient.

  Ⓑ embarrass the recipient.

  Ⓒ be written rather than spoken.

  Ⓓ be very imaginative.

22. A traveler might be <u>accompanied</u> by

  Ⓐ a friend.

  Ⓑ a travel agency.

  Ⓒ a hotel.

  Ⓓ his or her workplace.

23. Alyssa <u>supplemented</u> her dinner with

  Ⓐ a good book.

  Ⓑ a bedtime snack.

  Ⓒ a short nap.

  Ⓓ cleaning up the kitchen.

24. Someone in <u>captivity</u> is most likely to dream of

    Ⓐ   earning more money.

    Ⓑ   doing heroic deeds.

    Ⓒ   making new friends.

    Ⓓ   being set free.

25. I couldn't <u>interpret</u> his expression. <u>Interpret</u> means

    Ⓐ   figure out the meaning of.

    Ⓑ   bear to look at.

    Ⓒ   forget.

    Ⓓ   mimic exactly.

26. The chimp was trained to <u>retrieve</u> a ball. It would

    Ⓐ   throw the ball at a basketball hoop.

    Ⓑ   make a sign for the word *ball*.

    Ⓒ   bring back the ball you had just thrown.

    Ⓓ   hide the ball under a piece of furniture.

27. The cats <u>skirmished</u> and then ran. <u>Skirmished</u> means

    Ⓐ   ate quickly.

    Ⓑ   jumped outside.

    Ⓒ   jumped up.

    Ⓓ   had a short fight.

28. When Alaska was a <u>territory</u> and not a state, it was

    Ⓐ   an independent country.

    Ⓑ   governed by the United States.

    Ⓒ   able to elect its own president.

    Ⓓ   part of the state of Washington.

Book 6, Lesson 9 Test

Find a SYNONYM for each underlined word. Then fill in the circle next to your answer.

1. Molasses may be a <u>substitute</u> for brown sugar.

   Ⓐ supplement

   Ⓑ ingredient

   Ⓒ replacement

   Ⓓ term

2. The world's rainforests are <u>diminishing</u>.

   Ⓐ expanding

   Ⓑ shrinking

   Ⓒ deteriorating

   Ⓓ withering

3. Some chemicals <u>contaminate</u> water.

   Ⓐ pollute

   Ⓑ dye

   Ⓒ filter

   Ⓓ disinfect

4. The tundra <u>sustains</u> a limited variety of wildlife.

   Ⓐ welcomes

   Ⓑ encloses

   Ⓒ shelters

   Ⓓ supports

5. The path along the cliffs is <u>perilous</u>.

   Ⓐ scenic

   Ⓑ dangerous

   Ⓒ windy

   Ⓓ secure

6. We should <u>conserve</u> our wilderness areas.

   Ⓐ   explore

   Ⓑ   map

   Ⓒ   preserve

   Ⓓ   appreciate

7. Her exotic vacation plans encouraged <u>extravagance</u>.

   Ⓐ   banking

   Ⓑ   saving

   Ⓒ   budgeting

   Ⓓ   overspending

Find an ANTONYM for each underlined word. Then fill in the circle next to your answer.

8. The program host <u>aggravates</u> the viewers.

   Ⓐ   captivates

   Ⓑ   irritates

   Ⓒ   ignores

   Ⓓ   silences

9. A new grade school is <u>vital</u>.

   Ⓐ   unplanned

   Ⓑ   unnecessary

   Ⓒ   required

   Ⓓ   important

10. Hospitals must guard against <u>contamination</u>.

   Ⓐ   knowledge

   Ⓑ   carefulness

   Ⓒ   emergencies

   Ⓓ   cleanliness

11. Carlos made <u>drastic</u> changes in his life.

   Ⓐ   unneeded

   Ⓑ   foolish

   Ⓒ   modest

   Ⓓ   dramatic

12. Stephanie is <u>resourceful</u> in a crisis.

    Ⓐ   aggressive

    Ⓑ   grim

    Ⓒ   positive

    Ⓓ   helpless

13. The dictator continued to <u>accumulate</u> wealth.

    Ⓐ   distribute

    Ⓑ   add

    Ⓒ   reveal

    Ⓓ   praise

Choose the BEST way to complete each sentence or answer each question. Then fill in the circle next to your answer.

14. What would be an <u>aggravation</u> to a mail carrier?

    Ⓐ   post cards

    Ⓑ   snarling dogs

    Ⓒ   a new mail truck

    Ⓓ   a shorter route

15. A <u>vital</u> personality is

    Ⓐ   breathing.

    Ⓑ   clever.

    Ⓒ   spirited.

    Ⓓ   imaginative.

16. What could be <u>substituted</u> for a rain hat?

    Ⓐ   an umbrella

    Ⓑ   a pair of rain boots

    Ⓒ   a rain storm

    Ⓓ   windshield wipers

17. If there are <u>impurities</u> in water, it means that the water contains

    Ⓐ   flavorings.

    Ⓑ   small amounts of dirt.

    Ⓒ   carbonation.

    Ⓓ   sugar.

18. The necklace was an <u>extravagance</u>. An <u>extravagance</u> is

     Ⓐ   a purchase you can't afford.

     Ⓑ   an item that does not meet a basic need.

     Ⓒ   an item that is beautifully made.

     Ⓓ   an item you have been saving for.

19. <u>Peril</u> is involved in pearl diving. <u>Peril</u> means

     Ⓐ   skillfulness.

     Ⓑ   bravery.

     Ⓒ   danger.

     Ⓓ   control.

20. The lost hiker drew on all his <u>resources</u>. <u>Resources</u> are

     Ⓐ   savings in the bank.

     Ⓑ   water and minerals.

     Ⓒ   skills at dealing with problems.

     Ⓓ   family and friends.

21. A <u>substitute</u> pitcher is someone who is

     Ⓐ   not as good as the regular pitcher.

     Ⓑ   filling in for the regular pitcher.

     Ⓒ   better than the regular pitcher.

     Ⓓ   on the opposite team.

22. <u>Perpetual</u> is to time as

     Ⓐ   calendar is to clock.

     Ⓑ   day is to minute.

     Ⓒ   endless is to space.

     Ⓓ   brief is to hour.

23. What could <u>aggravate</u> a headache?

     Ⓐ   lying down in the dark

     Ⓑ   taking an aspirin

     Ⓒ   riding a noisy bus

     Ⓓ   closing a window

24. A <u>frugal</u> person is likely to

    Ⓐ   spend money carelessly.

    Ⓑ   be a good cook.

    Ⓒ   have no friends.

    Ⓓ   reuse paper bags.

25. Justin <u>sustained</u> a strained back. <u>Sustained</u> means

    Ⓐ   convalesced from.

    Ⓑ   suffered from.

    Ⓒ   got treatment for.

    Ⓓ   caused.

26. What could <u>imperil</u> pedestrians?

    Ⓐ   a skateboarder on the sidewalk

    Ⓑ   an interesting shop window

    Ⓒ   a crosswalk

    Ⓓ   a bus stop

27. It was <u>vital</u> that they find shelter. <u>Vital</u> means

    Ⓐ   likely.

    Ⓑ   very important.

    Ⓒ   impossible.

    Ⓓ   certain.

28. The aim of energy <u>conservation</u> is to

    Ⓐ   use wilderness resources to create energy.

    Ⓑ   force energy suppliers to lower their bills.

    Ⓒ   save energy by carefully using it.

    Ⓓ   create more energy by different means.

29. Rudeness is to <u>aggravation</u> as

    Ⓐ   sleep is to wakefulness.

    Ⓑ   laughter is to mirth.

    Ⓒ   mischief is to apologies.

    Ⓓ   exercise is to exhaustion.

30. What would be an <u>extravagant</u> act for the average person?

    Ⓐ   having friends over for dinner

    Ⓑ   going out for a pizza

    Ⓒ   building a castle

    Ⓓ   washing the dishes

31. Which of these is a natural <u>resource</u>?

    Ⓐ   money in a savings account

    Ⓑ   oil

    Ⓒ   bread

    Ⓓ   sand

Book 6, Lesson 10 Test

Find a SYNONYM for each underlined word. Then fill in the circle next to your answer.

1. Amber gave a <u>brief</u> summary of the plot.

   Ⓐ thorough
   Ⓑ short
   Ⓒ painstaking
   Ⓓ confusing

2. Closing off the street was an <u>error</u>.

   Ⓐ necessity
   Ⓑ requirement
   Ⓒ mistake
   Ⓓ failure

3. Sean <u>griped</u> for the first two days of camp.

   Ⓐ sulked
   Ⓑ boasted
   Ⓒ sneered
   Ⓓ complained

4. The medicine <u>effected</u> a cure.

   Ⓐ defeated
   Ⓑ thwarted
   Ⓒ prevented
   Ⓓ produced

5. She has a <u>knack</u> for making jewelry.

   Ⓐ education
   Ⓑ teacher
   Ⓒ talent
   Ⓓ class

6. They ate a <u>leisurely</u> dinner.

- Ⓐ delicious
- Ⓑ relaxed
- Ⓒ light
- Ⓓ formal

7. Convenience was a <u>factor</u> in making the decision.

- Ⓐ limit
- Ⓑ issue
- Ⓒ strength
- Ⓓ hurdle

8. There was a <u>fad</u> for wearing old felt hats.

- Ⓐ club
- Ⓑ place
- Ⓒ get-together
- Ⓓ trend

Find an ANTONYM for each underlined word. Then fill in the circle next to your answer.

9. A <u>brisk</u> walk on the beach will do you good.

- Ⓐ noisy
- Ⓑ warm
- Ⓒ unhurried
- Ⓓ short

10. The firm is <u>bankrupt</u>.

- Ⓐ prosperous
- Ⓑ failing
- Ⓒ well-known
- Ⓓ notable

11. The companies <u>competed</u> to get the contract.

- Ⓐ skirmished
- Ⓑ debated
- Ⓒ cooperated
- Ⓓ bid

12. The solution is <u>complicated</u>.

   Ⓐ   difficult

   Ⓑ   undiscovered

   Ⓒ   worthless

   Ⓓ   obvious

13. The author has a <u>unique</u> point of view.

   Ⓐ   strange

   Ⓑ   common

   Ⓒ   sensible

   Ⓓ   exasperating

14. We have been <u>anticipating</u> our vacation.

   Ⓐ   dreading

   Ⓑ   enjoying

   Ⓒ   wasting

   Ⓓ   shortening

15. Planting in raised beds is an <u>effective</u> way to garden.

   Ⓐ   unknown

   Ⓑ   ordinary

   Ⓒ   useless

   Ⓓ   tiring

16. Their conclusion was <u>erroneous</u>.

   Ⓐ   absurd

   Ⓑ   stupid

   Ⓒ   simple

   Ⓓ   correct

Choose the BEST way to complete each sentence or answer each question. Then fill in the circle next to your answer.

17. <u>Budget</u> is to time as

   Ⓐ   work is to money.

   Ⓑ   conserve is to energy.

   Ⓒ   bungle is to mistake.

   Ⓓ   consume is to gorge.

18. The captain <u>briefed</u> the soldiers. This means that he

Ⓐ gave them orders.

Ⓑ took them to court.

Ⓒ questioned them.

Ⓓ criticized them.

19. The law is not yet <u>effective</u>. This means that it

Ⓐ has not been proposed.

Ⓑ is too weak to be useful.

Ⓒ is frequently disobeyed.

Ⓓ is not yet being enforced.

20. The old king was <u>bankrupt</u> of morals. This means that he

Ⓐ had done too many moral acts.

Ⓑ no longer noticed what others did.

Ⓒ had no morals left.

Ⓓ had nothing left to say on the subject.

21. A <u>competition</u> ends when

Ⓐ it runs out of money.

Ⓑ someone wins.

Ⓒ everyone goes home.

Ⓓ everyone loses interest.

22. High rents <u>gripe</u> local citizens. <u>Gripe</u> means

Ⓐ separate.

Ⓑ inflict.

Ⓒ irritate.

Ⓓ enrich.

23. Which of the following is likely to be <u>brisk</u>?

Ⓐ a heavy coat

Ⓑ a plate of pancakes

Ⓒ a pet parrot

Ⓓ an autumn wind

24. A lawyer's <u>brief</u> is similar to

    Ⓐ a summary.

    Ⓑ a taunt.

    Ⓒ a challenge.

    Ⓓ an extract.

25. <u>Anticipating</u> rain, she took an umbrella. This means that she

    Ⓐ was eagerly looking forward to rain.

    Ⓑ disliked rain.

    Ⓒ expected rain and prepared for it.

    Ⓓ always knew when it was going to rain.

26. The <u>effects</u> of the storm were still unknown. <u>Effects</u> are

    Ⓐ the main features of something.

    Ⓑ the expanses it covered.

    Ⓒ important details.

    Ⓓ results.

27. Allison <u>erred</u> in leaving the door unlocked. <u>Erred</u> means

    Ⓐ made a mistake.

    Ⓑ was forgetful.

    Ⓒ did great damage.

    Ⓓ betrayed someone's trust.

28. <u>Competitor</u> is to race as

    Ⓐ actor is to performance.

    Ⓑ cook is to breakfast.

    Ⓒ sailor is to captain.

    Ⓓ optimist is to trouble.

29. Sticking to a <u>budget</u> should

    Ⓐ keep you from getting lost.

    Ⓑ protect you from extravagance.

    Ⓒ present obstacles.

    Ⓓ discourage frivolous ideas.

30. What might cause someone to have a <u>gripe</u>?

    Ⓐ   the arrival of a new movie in the theater

    Ⓑ   germs floating in the air

    Ⓒ   a new car that breaks down

    Ⓓ   frequent exercise

31. To <u>complicate</u> a problem is to

    Ⓐ   analyze it.

    Ⓑ   take it apart.

    Ⓒ   overcome it.

    Ⓓ   make it more confusing.

32. Victoria wrote an <u>effective</u> letter to the editor. This means that it

    Ⓐ   made a strong, positive impression.

    Ⓑ   was very aggressive.

    Ⓒ   showed her exasperation.

    Ⓓ   identified many problems.

33. What could <u>bankrupt</u> a person?

    Ⓐ   running on an icy sidewalk

    Ⓑ   watching too much television

    Ⓒ   spending money carelessly

    Ⓓ   eating unhealthy foods

34. Nathan sees everything in terms of <u>competition</u>. It is important to him

    Ⓐ   to stay involved in sports.

    Ⓑ   spend a lot of time with others.

    Ⓒ   watch a lot of sports on television.

    Ⓓ   to win.

35. What is a typical way to spend <u>leisure</u> time?

    Ⓐ   working overtime

    Ⓑ   relaxing with a good book

    Ⓒ   making photocopies

    Ⓓ   returning phone calls

Book 6, Midterm Test 1 (Lessons 1–10)

Read the passage. Choose the BEST answer for each sentence or question about an underlined word. Then fill in the circle next to your answer.

THE 1939 NEW YORK WORLD'S FAIR

The New York World's Fair, which opened on April 30, 1939, <u>eclipsed</u> all previous international fairs. It was the most expensive fair to date, costing more than 150 million dollars to build. It was also the biggest, covering 1,256 acres of land that included a river and lake. This vast <u>expanse</u> was created by filling in a city dump in Flushing Meadows, Queens. Ten thousand trees and one million tulips were planted in the landfill. There were 300 substantial buildings put up on the site to house 1,500 <u>exhibits</u> from 58 foreign countries, 33 states, and 1,300 companies. The immense symbol of the fair, a tower shaped like a tall, skinny triangle together with a giant globe, was the sight that welcomed guests to the fairgrounds. The triangular tower was higher than the Washington Monument, and the globe was as high as an eighteen-story building.

During the fair's two-year run, a <u>continuous</u> stream of visitors poured through its gates. About forty-five million people came to view the fair's <u>incredible</u> sights and amusements. There was something for everyone, from thrilling rides like the parachute jump to displays of the latest scientific inventions. Fair-goers could watch cows being milked on a merry-go-round or take a ride on the Road of Tomorrow. Countries from around the world presented their arts and crafts as well as their achievements in science and industry.

The name of the fair was "The World of Tomorrow," which reflected the United States's optimism about the future. The fair's creators believed that what had been <u>attained</u> so far was nothing compared to what would come to pass in the near future. Science-based business exhibits celebrated the <u>triumphs</u> of technology and predicted new uses for the world's natural <u>resources</u>. One of the earliest television programs was broadcast from the fair to the very few people in New York City who had TV sets.

The most popular feature of the fair was the <u>unique</u> Futurama exhibit. <u>Hordes</u> of people stood in line for hours to enter it. This 3,600-square-foot exhibit was a <u>realistic</u> scale model showing an area of the United States as it might be in 1960. The model city included 1,500-foot-high buildings that were like small cities in themselves. Inhabitants would live, work, and shop in the same building. There were parklands and small towns outside the model city. Visitors to Futurama were carried in moving chairs past animated displays while a sound device in each chair told them what to <u>anticipate</u> in the future.

The exhibit's makers correctly predicted that telescopes would become amazingly powerful and that freeways would dominate our landscapes. However, they also predicted that many people would live outside the cities in one-factory farm villages. They thought that liquid air would power vehicles, and that energy would arrive in homes by means of radio waves. Today, some of their predictions seem foolish and even childish to us. Yet we, too, share some of their dreams. Like them, we hope that a cure for cancer will be a part of the future and that our natural resources will be protected and wisely used.

1. In this passage, eclipsed means

   Ⓐ   outshone.
   Ⓑ   hid.
   Ⓒ   saw.
   Ⓓ   outspent.

2. An expanse refers to

   Ⓐ   money paid out.
   Ⓑ   fencing.
   Ⓒ   a stretch of land.
   Ⓓ   a small city.

3. Exhibits are

   Ⓐ   guests.
   Ⓑ   works of art.
   Ⓒ   entertainment devices.
   Ⓓ   displays.

4. A continuous stream of visitors is one that

   Ⓐ   is sparse.
   Ⓑ   doesn't seem to stop.
   Ⓒ   acts boisterous.
   Ⓓ   seems very eager.

5. Visitors found the fair's sights incredible. This means that

   Ⓐ   they decided what they saw was not real.
   Ⓑ   it was hard for them to believe in what they saw.
   Ⓒ   the sights made them thoughtful.
   Ⓓ   they found the sites notable.

6. In this passage, attained means

   Ⓐ   got.
   Ⓑ   invented.
   Ⓒ   achieved.
   Ⓓ   imagined.

7. An antonym for <u>triumphs</u> is

   Ⓐ accomplishments.

   Ⓑ questions.

   Ⓒ monotony.

   Ⓓ failures.

8. In this passage, <u>resources</u> refers to

   Ⓐ clear ideas about solving problems.

   Ⓑ supplies of materials that can be used when needed.

   Ⓒ survival skills.

   Ⓓ unsettled territories.

9. The Futurama exhibit was <u>unique</u>. <u>Unique</u> means

   Ⓐ a good idea.

   Ⓑ very popular.

   Ⓒ brilliantly crafted.

   Ⓓ the only one of its kind.

10. Which of the following is a synonym for <u>hordes</u>?

    Ⓐ crowds

    Ⓑ lines

    Ⓒ mixtures

    Ⓓ armies

11. The exhibit was a <u>realistic</u> scale model. <u>Realistic</u> means

    Ⓐ practical.

    Ⓑ alive.

    Ⓒ lifelike.

    Ⓓ smaller than life.

12. In this passage, <u>anticipate</u> means

    Ⓐ dread.

    Ⓑ expect.

    Ⓒ attempt.

    Ⓓ bring about.

Book 6, Midterm Test 2 (Lessons 1–10)

Read the passage. Choose the BEST answer for each sentence or question about an underlined word. Then fill in the circle next to your answer.

COSTUME IN THE FRENCH COURT

From 1643 to 1715, the reign of Louis XIV, wealthy French people had no <u>function</u> in government and rarely had to work outside the home. These bored nobles lived in or near the king's palace and spent all their time at court. They devoted their lives to finding ways to pass their <u>leisure</u> hours and show off their wealth. They did both by wearing <u>splendid</u> <u>attire</u> that they sometimes changed several times a day.

Dressing well was quite an art. Men and women's <u>apparel</u> was made of rich fabrics and decorated with expensive trims. At that time, cotton was a luxury fabric, along with satin and velvet. Cotton was a luxury because unlike today, it was imported and was quite scarce. Although men's clothing was not as fussy as it had been in earlier years, it was still heavily trimmed in gold and silver embroidery and braid. In 1644, a Paris merchant figured out how to color glass like precious gems, and these fake jewels, as well as real ones, were strewn like stars on men's outfits as well as on women's. Lace, too, was very popular and was worn as trim around necklines, cuffs, and even at the hems of men's breeches. Chinese silk stockings covered in patterns came into fashion in the 1670s. Some <u>superb</u> articles of clothing have survived from this period, densely covered with designs in gold and colored thread. Fruit, flowers, birds, and insects that seemed to come from fairy-tale gardens were popular designs. Amazingly, some of this clothing, such as wonderfully decorated men's vests, was sometimes made for ordinary daily use and not just for court <u>ceremonies</u>.

Both men and women wore fancy hairstyles to complement their clothing. Men wore wigs, a trend that <u>originated</u> with the previous king, Louis XIII, who had lost a lot of hair during an illness. At first the wigs were blended with the man's own hair. Over time, the wigs became fuller and thicker, and men had to shave their heads in order to wear the wigs. The wigs rose up high, curled over their wearer's shoulders in thick clouds, and sometimes <u>extended</u> to their waists. Women wore their hair in <u>lofty</u> styles, sometimes as much as a foot high. Their hair was arranged on brass wire frames and woven through with ribbons and lace. These ornaments were <u>supplemented</u> with flowers, bows, and even tiny figures. Some women went so far as to have their hairdressers create miniature landscapes in their hair, complete with tiny ships. Although cartoonists made fun of this hairstyle, it remained popular for about thirty years.

Although styles changed, <u>extravagant</u> dress remained fashionable for many decades since it was one of the most obvious means of showing off wealth and taste. In 1789, during the reign of Louis XVI, the French lower and middle classes rose up and successfully rebelled.

One of the reasons for their anger was that bread was scarce because so much flour was used up to powder men's wigs and women's hairstyles. When a republic of the people was established, court dress was outlawed and simpler clothes became more popular.

1. In the story, <u>function</u> means

   Ⓐ important gathering.

   Ⓑ position.

   Ⓒ power.

   Ⓓ purpose.

2. <u>Leisure</u> time refers to

   Ⓐ time spent working.

   Ⓑ time spent away from home.

   Ⓒ time not taken up by work.

   Ⓓ time used for shopping.

3. A synonym for <u>splendid</u> is

   Ⓐ nice.

   Ⓑ magnificent.

   Ⓒ pretty.

   Ⓓ costly.

4. Which of the following is a type of <u>attire</u>?

   Ⓐ a velvet skirt

   Ⓑ a poodle

   Ⓒ a luxury car

   Ⓓ diamond earrings

5. A synonym for <u>apparel</u> is

   Ⓐ curtains.

   Ⓑ table linens.

   Ⓒ furniture.

   Ⓓ clothing.

6. A <u>superb</u> article of clothing is

   Ⓐ very old.

   Ⓑ in good condition.

   Ⓒ outstanding.

   Ⓓ flashy.

7. Which one of the following is a <u>ceremony</u>?

    Ⓐ   a wedding

    Ⓑ   a bike ride

    Ⓒ   a book club meeting

    Ⓓ   spending a week at summer camp

8. In this passage, <u>originated</u> means

    Ⓐ   declined.

    Ⓑ   brought into style.

    Ⓒ   became a law.

    Ⓓ   substituted.

9. Men's wigs sometimes <u>extended</u> to their waists. <u>Extended</u> means

    Ⓐ   made longer.

    Ⓑ   offered.

    Ⓒ   reached.

    Ⓓ   lay.

10. In this passage, <u>lofty</u> means

    Ⓐ   high.

    Ⓑ   noble.

    Ⓒ   proud.

    Ⓓ   cloudlike.

11. The puffs of hair were <u>supplemented</u> by other ornaments. <u>Supplemented</u> means

    Ⓐ   replaced.

    Ⓑ   weighed down.

    Ⓒ   furnished.

    Ⓓ   added to.

12. An antonym for <u>extravagant</u> is

    Ⓐ   plain.

    Ⓑ   frugal.

    Ⓒ   primitive.

    Ⓓ   unfashionable.

Book 6, Lesson 11 Test

Find a SYNONYM for each underlined word. Then fill in the circle next to your answer.

1. You should <u>persevere</u> in learning the guitar.

   Ⓐ persist

   Ⓑ improve

   Ⓒ hurry

   Ⓓ resign

2. Their attempt to save the harvest was <u>futile</u>.

   Ⓐ skillful

   Ⓑ premature

   Ⓒ successful

   Ⓓ hopeless

3. You'll need to <u>abbreviate</u> your speech.

   Ⓐ simplify

   Ⓑ illuminate

   Ⓒ shorten

   Ⓓ soften

4. The television program made Leo <u>sneer</u>.

   Ⓐ laugh

   Ⓑ scorn

   Ⓒ frown

   Ⓓ smile

5. The group expressed <u>unanimity</u> on the issue.

   Ⓐ disagreement

   Ⓑ determination

   Ⓒ agreement

   Ⓓ uncertainty

6. The soldiers felt <u>grudging</u> respect for their enemy.

    Ⓐ   enthusiastic

    Ⓑ   somber

    Ⓒ   intense

    Ⓓ   unwilling

7. Anxiety <u>possessed</u> her as she stepped on stage.

    Ⓐ   halted

    Ⓑ   overcame

    Ⓒ   left

    Ⓓ   stunned

Find an ANTONYM for each underlined word. Then fill in the circle next to your answer.

8. Richard is <u>resolute</u> on this matter.

    Ⓐ   unsure

    Ⓑ   firm

    Ⓒ   thoughtful

    Ⓓ   careless

9. Her <u>fanciful</u> plans had no supporters.

    Ⓐ   celebrated

    Ⓑ   elaborate

    Ⓒ   practical

    Ⓓ   uninteresting

10. Kelly <u>possesses</u> an outstanding character.

    Ⓐ   dislikes

    Ⓑ   lacks

    Ⓒ   respects

    Ⓓ   values

11. The contract should <u>exclude</u> references to age.

    Ⓐ   add

    Ⓑ   stress

    Ⓒ   contain

    Ⓓ   leave out

12. Amber murmured some <u>appropriate</u> words to the guest of honor.

    Ⓐ   loud

    Ⓑ   hilarious

    Ⓒ   honest

    Ⓓ   unsuitable

13. Three <u>unruly</u> boys got on the bus.

    Ⓐ   well-behaved

    Ⓑ   well-dressed

    Ⓒ   friendly

    Ⓓ   sluggish

Choose the BEST way to complete each sentence or answer each question. Then fill in the circle next to your answer.

14. The lawyer's brief said that the jury was <u>prejudiced</u>. This means that the jury

    Ⓐ   carefully considered all the facts in the case.

    Ⓑ   made their decision without considering all the facts.

    Ⓒ   returned a verdict of not guilty.

    Ⓓ   could not reach a verdict.

15. <u>Majority</u> is to most as

    Ⓐ   pound is to weigh.

    Ⓑ   final is to last.

    Ⓒ   average is to least.

    Ⓓ   meager is to abundant.

16. Your <u>possessions</u> are

    Ⓐ   your character traits.

    Ⓑ   the things that you use.

    Ⓒ   the things that you own.

    Ⓓ   the people you are related to.

17. There was strong <u>prejudice</u> against the new ideas. <u>Prejudice</u> is

    Ⓐ   lively debate.

    Ⓑ   proof.

    Ⓒ   a judgment made without facts.

    Ⓓ   a group of opponents.

18. Nicole's <u>sneers</u> were clearly intended as

Ⓐ warnings.

Ⓑ encouragement.

Ⓒ approval.

Ⓓ insults.

19. Which of the following is an <u>abbreviation</u>?

Ⓐ cab

Ⓑ Dr.

Ⓒ Miss

Ⓓ bug

20. Some tax money is <u>appropriated</u> for fire protection. <u>Appropriated</u> means

Ⓐ set aside.

Ⓑ taken illegally.

Ⓒ divided.

Ⓓ passed around.

21. Nathan's long hair <u>prejudiced</u> the interviewers. His hair

Ⓐ distracted them from his words.

Ⓑ amazed them.

Ⓒ caused them to have an unfair opinion of him.

Ⓓ made them envious.

22. Mr. Garcia <u>inspired</u> Gabrielle to go to college. This means he

Ⓐ paid her way to college.

Ⓑ ordered her to go.

Ⓒ argued her into going.

Ⓓ got her excited about the idea.

23. Which of the following shows <u>perseverance</u>?

Ⓐ deciding to learn to use a skateboard

Ⓑ practicing something until one is very good at it

Ⓒ speaking sharply to a store clerk

Ⓓ helping a friend shop for shoes

24. To be in <u>possession</u> of a fine house is to

    Ⓐ feel envious of its owners.

    Ⓑ live nearby.

    Ⓒ own it.

    Ⓓ be a welcome visitor to it.

25. Austin has a <u>grudge</u> against his boss. This means that he

    Ⓐ has caught his boss doing something against the law.

    Ⓑ knows something that his boss doesn't.

    Ⓒ argues constantly with his boss.

    Ⓓ resents his boss.

26. Which of the following is a <u>unanimous</u> vote in favor of something?

    Ⓐ 8 for; 2 against

    Ⓑ 10 for; 0 against

    Ⓒ 5 for; 5 against

    Ⓓ 1 for; 9 against

27. Which of the following might be <u>unruly</u>?

    Ⓐ a broken yardstick

    Ⓑ curly hair

    Ⓒ unlined paper

    Ⓓ sleeping kittens

28. The picture book shows a <u>fanciful</u> landscape. <u>Fanciful</u> means

    Ⓐ imaginary.

    Ⓑ forested.

    Ⓒ densely populated.

    Ⓓ not very practical.

29. The writer lacks <u>inspiration</u>. This means that the writer

    Ⓐ has not been recently paid.

    Ⓑ gets no encouragement from family and friends.

    Ⓒ is not very talented.

    Ⓓ has no ideas that seem exciting or worthwhile.

30. The mean farmer <u>grudged</u> his nephew his meals. <u>Grudged</u> means

    Ⓐ gave unwillingly.

    Ⓑ prepared.

    Ⓒ charged.

    Ⓓ kept track of.

31. Anthony won by a <u>majority</u> of nine. This means that

    Ⓐ there were nine candidates, and Anthony got the most votes.

    Ⓑ he got nine votes and the other candidate got two.

    Ⓒ he got nine more votes than the other candidate.

    Ⓓ nine important people supported his campaign.

Book 6, Lesson 12 Test

Find a SYNONYM for each underlined word. Then fill in the circle next to your answer.

1. It takes two people to <u>haul</u> the net.

    Ⓐ toss

    Ⓑ secure

    Ⓒ pull

    Ⓓ repair

2. Andrea was the <u>victor</u>.

    Ⓐ seller

    Ⓑ best

    Ⓒ chief

    Ⓓ winner

3. Erika <u>scoffed</u> when she heard Jordan's explanation.

    Ⓐ smiled

    Ⓑ sneered

    Ⓒ sympathized

    Ⓓ disbelieved

4. The problem <u>baffled</u> both students.

    Ⓐ interested

    Ⓑ involved

    Ⓒ confused

    Ⓓ required

5. He paid dearly for his <u>blunder</u>.

    Ⓐ purchase

    Ⓑ error

    Ⓒ safety

    Ⓓ peace

6. Their faces were <u>woeful</u>.

    Ⓐ sorrowful

    Ⓑ grim

    Ⓒ lively

    Ⓓ calm

7. The actor made a <u>sinister</u> gesture.

    Ⓐ shy

    Ⓑ meaningful

    Ⓒ threatening

    Ⓓ unusual

Find an ANTONYM for each underlined word. Then fill in the circle next to your answer.

8. Sam <u>abandoned</u> his scheme to get rich.

    Ⓐ developed

    Ⓑ withheld

    Ⓒ abbreviated

    Ⓓ retained

9. Morgan <u>detected</u> the flaw in the problem.

    Ⓐ noticed

    Ⓑ challenged

    Ⓒ provided

    Ⓓ overlooked

10. The <u>adversaries</u> met in a dark alley.

    Ⓐ strangers

    Ⓑ friends

    Ⓒ relatives

    Ⓓ competitors

11. One <u>sentinel</u> stood at the gate.

    Ⓐ guard

    Ⓑ soldier

    Ⓒ spy

    Ⓓ major

12. The horror movie featured a <u>colossal</u> fly.

    Ⓐ minute

    Ⓑ harmless

    Ⓒ charming

    Ⓓ weak

13. The couple <u>blundered</u> through the dance.

    Ⓐ waddled

    Ⓑ jumped

    Ⓒ glided

    Ⓓ twisted

Choose the BEST way to complete each sentence or answer each question. Then fill in the circle next to your answer.

14. Which of the following should be <u>abandoned</u>?

    Ⓐ a house in the path of a flood

    Ⓑ a windstorm

    Ⓒ a new rowboat

    Ⓓ a celebration

15. What could be found in a <u>haul</u>?

    Ⓐ moving boxes

    Ⓑ crabs

    Ⓒ a soccer team

    Ⓓ laundry

16. Brooding on your <u>woes</u> is useless. <u>Woes</u> means

    Ⓐ romances.

    Ⓑ debts.

    Ⓒ misfortunes.

    Ⓓ faults.

17. A <u>victorious</u> general is one who

    Ⓐ speaks fluently.

    Ⓑ has retired from the army.

    Ⓒ fought in a foreign war.

    Ⓓ has won a battle.

18. Anna <u>overpowered</u> the other debaters. This means that she

    Ⓐ   threw them on the ground.

    Ⓑ   got the best of them in arguments.

    Ⓒ   spoke louder than anyone else.

    Ⓓ   gave in to their more powerful arguments.

19. What might someone <u>rejoice</u> over?

    Ⓐ   getting accepted into college

    Ⓑ   watching an interesting show

    Ⓒ   getting a slight sunburn

    Ⓓ   losing a wallet

20. Which of the following may face long <u>hauls</u>?

    Ⓐ   teenagers applying for drivers' licenses

    Ⓑ   sailors taking boats out on the bay

    Ⓒ   drivers of moving vans

    Ⓓ   students studying for tests

21. Richard <u>blundered</u> by telling her about the party. <u>Blundered</u> means

    Ⓐ   shocked someone.

    Ⓑ   did someone a favor.

    Ⓒ   made a mistake.

    Ⓓ   made up for an earlier mistake.

22. The refugees lacked words to tell of their <u>woes</u>. <u>Woes</u> are

    Ⓐ   miseries.

    Ⓑ   needs.

    Ⓒ   abilities.

    Ⓓ   inconveniences.

23. The college had to <u>abandon</u> the daycare program. This means that

    Ⓐ   they had to leave the collapsing building.

    Ⓑ   they had to provide more funds for it.

    Ⓒ   they had to reassess its needs.

    Ⓓ   they had to withdraw their support.

24. A <u>siege</u> is usually conducted by

    Ⓐ   an orchestra.

    Ⓑ   an army.

    Ⓒ   a detailed map.

    Ⓓ   a scout leader.

25. It was a <u>woeful</u> mistake to drop out of school. <u>Woeful</u> means

    Ⓐ   selfish.

    Ⓑ   thoughtless.

    Ⓒ   very bad.

    Ⓓ   foolish.

Book 6, Lesson 13 Test

Find a SYNONYM for each underlined word. Then fill in the circle next to your answer.

1. Patrick is <u>oblivious</u> to danger.

   - Ⓐ reckless
   - Ⓑ unaware
   - Ⓒ accustomed
   - Ⓓ drawn

2. We are rapidly <u>depleting</u> our oil resources.

   - Ⓐ renewing
   - Ⓑ converting
   - Ⓒ consuming
   - Ⓓ exploiting

3. The Galvez family <u>adapted</u> to the hotter climate.

   - Ⓐ immigrated
   - Ⓑ protested
   - Ⓒ submitted
   - Ⓓ adjusted

4. Mr. Lyons has a hesitant <u>gait</u>.

   - Ⓐ manner
   - Ⓑ commitment
   - Ⓒ walk
   - Ⓓ speech

5. This computer is <u>outmoded</u>.

   - Ⓐ fast
   - Ⓑ out-of-date
   - Ⓒ sluggish
   - Ⓓ extravagant

6. The exhibit shows the beavers' <u>habitat</u>.

    Ⓐ environment

    Ⓑ appearance

    Ⓒ practices

    Ⓓ life cycle

7. How will they <u>transport</u> the statue?

    Ⓐ raise

    Ⓑ move

    Ⓒ construct

    Ⓓ carve

8. There was a <u>glaring</u> error in the problem.

    Ⓐ deliberate

    Ⓑ obscure

    Ⓒ upsetting

    Ⓓ obvious

Find an ANTONYM for each underlined word. Then fill in the circle next to your answer.

9. Just the thought of the hike filled me with <u>fatigue</u>.

    Ⓐ boredom

    Ⓑ reluctance

    Ⓒ energy

    Ⓓ pleasure

10. The Khans are a <u>prominent</u> family.

    Ⓐ frugal

    Ⓑ unknown

    Ⓒ grudging

    Ⓓ wealthy

11. Firefighters go through <u>rigorous</u> training.

    Ⓐ easy

    Ⓑ brief

    Ⓒ mental

    Ⓓ fanciful

12. The two girls <u>glared</u> at one another.

    Ⓐ   nodded

    Ⓑ   peeked

    Ⓒ   frowned

    Ⓓ   grinned

13. This play is an <u>adaptation</u>.

    Ⓐ   failure

    Ⓑ   original

    Ⓒ   translation

    Ⓓ   sensation

14. The hot winds <u>seared</u> the plains.

    Ⓐ   dried

    Ⓑ   stilled

    Ⓒ   soaked

    Ⓓ   battered

15. The performance <u>quenched</u> his dreams of becoming a rock star.

    Ⓐ   extinguished

    Ⓑ   decreased

    Ⓒ   conquered

    Ⓓ   revived

Choose the BEST way to complete each sentence or answer each question. Then fill in the circle next to your answer.

16. What might produce <u>oblivion</u>?

    Ⓐ   a hit song

    Ⓑ   a cloud passing over the sun

    Ⓒ   sleep

    Ⓓ   a stalled car in the road

17. To do something with <u>rigor</u> is to do it

    Ⓐ   in a straightforward way.

    Ⓑ   painstakingly.

    Ⓒ   cautiously.

    Ⓓ   strictly.

18. Which of these is <u>glaring</u>?

    Ⓐ a muddy lawn

    Ⓑ sun shining on ice

    Ⓒ a dim, faraway star

    Ⓓ a messy desktop

19. The curved handlebars are the bike's <u>prominent</u> feature. <u>Prominent</u> means

    Ⓐ most easily seen.

    Ⓑ most expensive.

    Ⓒ most popular.

    Ⓓ most requested.

20. Aaron got a <u>glare</u> from Melissa when he

    Ⓐ congratulated her on her test score.

    Ⓑ took her to a party.

    Ⓒ lent her his pen.

    Ⓓ nearly knocked her over.

21. To be <u>efficient</u> at work is to

    Ⓐ chat a lot with your coworkers.

    Ⓑ show up on time every day.

    Ⓒ take charge of a meeting.

    Ⓓ do your job without wasting time.

22. What might <u>fatigue</u> someone?

    Ⓐ treating a wound

    Ⓑ digging up ground for a garden

    Ⓒ ordering from a large menu

    Ⓓ paying an overdue bill

23. To <u>sear</u> a pork chop is to

    Ⓐ boil it.

    Ⓑ bake it in the oven.

    Ⓒ chop it up into chunks.

    Ⓓ quickly burn both sides.

24. When might someone encounter <u>rigors</u>?

    Ⓐ   during an art class

    Ⓑ   while putting together a jigsaw puzzle

    Ⓒ   while exploring the South Pole

    Ⓓ   during a visit to a museum

25. When you arrange for the <u>transport</u> of something, you arrange its

    Ⓐ   repair.

    Ⓑ   preparation to serve a different purpose.

    Ⓒ   change into an entirely new form.

    Ⓓ   move from one place to another.

26. Which of the following BEST describes a <u>glare</u>?

    Ⓐ   a blinking light

    Ⓑ   a twinkle

    Ⓒ   a shrouded light

    Ⓓ   a harsh, brilliant light

27. Which of the following can be seen <u>wending</u>?

    Ⓐ   a meadow

    Ⓑ   a river

    Ⓒ   a small town

    Ⓓ   a soft drink machine

28. Victor's <u>adaptation</u> to the new culture was quick. This means that he

    Ⓐ   soon came to dislike it.

    Ⓑ   quickly understood it.

    Ⓒ   quickly got used to living in it.

    Ⓓ   soon changed it to meet his needs.

29. Which of the following is <u>prominent</u>?

    Ⓐ   a popular book

    Ⓑ   a storm coming your way

    Ⓒ   a strong commitment

    Ⓓ   the only tall building in town

30. The best protection against something that <u>glares</u> is

    Ⓐ   an alarm.

    Ⓑ   dark sunglasses.

    Ⓒ   rubber boots.

    Ⓓ   a long stick.

31. Their music lessons were <u>rigorous</u>. <u>Rigorous</u> means

    Ⓐ   beneficial.

    Ⓑ   constant.

    Ⓒ   thorough.

    Ⓓ   unique.

32. How could someone <u>adapt</u> a bike for a child?

    Ⓐ   by sending it through a shipping company

    Ⓑ   by giving it as a birthday gift

    Ⓒ   by lowering the seat

    Ⓓ   by buying it used

33. What would BEST <u>quench</u> your thirst?

    Ⓐ   cold water

    Ⓑ   hot chocolate

    Ⓒ   a salty pretzel

    Ⓓ   a slice of watermelon

Book 6, Lesson 14 Test

Find a SYNONYM for each underlined word. Then fill in the circle next to your answer.

1. You will need your parents' <u>consent</u>.

   Ⓐ contribution
   Ⓑ permission
   Ⓒ advice
   Ⓓ opinion

2. Ms. Fujimoto was a <u>benevolent</u> employer.

   Ⓐ efficient
   Ⓑ rude
   Ⓒ kind
   Ⓓ grumpy

3. What is the spacecraft's <u>mission</u>?

   Ⓐ task
   Ⓑ path
   Ⓒ speed
   Ⓓ destination

4. His students <u>esteem</u> Professor Rosnov.

   Ⓐ degrade
   Ⓑ aggravate
   Ⓒ respect
   Ⓓ baffle

5. We had an <u>opportunity</u> to go to the Grand Canyon.

   Ⓐ arrangement
   Ⓑ plan
   Ⓒ longing
   Ⓓ chance

6. Dorothea Lange took <u>marvelous</u> photographs.

    Ⓐ realistic

    Ⓑ splendid

    Ⓒ shocking

    Ⓓ famous

7. The emperor was oblivious to <u>intrigues</u>.

    Ⓐ schemes

    Ⓑ discomforts

    Ⓒ woes

    Ⓓ problems

8. The Great Plains are <u>extensive</u>.

    Ⓐ fertile

    Ⓑ arid

    Ⓒ large

    Ⓓ conspicuous

Find an ANTONYM for each underlined word. Then fill in the circle next to your answer.

9. Dylan <u>relinquished</u> the trophy.

    Ⓐ enjoyed

    Ⓑ loathed

    Ⓒ returned

    Ⓓ kept

10. The lecture <u>engrossed</u> them.

    Ⓐ delighted

    Ⓑ bored

    Ⓒ confused

    Ⓓ inspired

11. The newscaster <u>exaggerated</u> the effects of the storm.

    Ⓐ understated

    Ⓑ whispered

    Ⓒ concealed

    Ⓓ praised

12. The movie's special effects were <u>fantastic</u>.

    Ⓐ monstrous

    Ⓑ resourceful

    Ⓒ ordinary

    Ⓓ invaluable

13. Hannah gave <u>discreet</u> replies to the competitor's questions.

    Ⓐ stern

    Ⓑ taunting

    Ⓒ simple

    Ⓓ unwise

14. Northern tribes <u>vanquished</u> the natives of Britain.

    Ⓐ enslaved

    Ⓑ freed

    Ⓒ eclipsed

    Ⓓ abandoned

15. They <u>marveled</u> at the Greek ruins.

    Ⓐ assembled

    Ⓑ sneered

    Ⓒ wondered

    Ⓓ gasped

Choose the BEST way to complete each sentence or answer each question. Then fill in the circle next to your answer.

16. <u>Tyrant</u> is to dictator as

    Ⓐ country is to border.

    Ⓑ blunder is to error.

    Ⓒ boycott is to business.

    Ⓓ fatigue is to rest.

17. The sunset yesterday evening was <u>marvelous</u>. <u>Marvelous</u> means

    Ⓐ red and orange

    Ⓑ unremarkable

    Ⓒ astonishing in its beauty

    Ⓓ obscured by haze

18. An <u>esteemed</u> writer is one

    Ⓐ   who is invited to a lot of functions.

    Ⓑ   whose work is respected.

    Ⓒ   who has written a great many books.

    Ⓓ   who is often criticized.

19. The <u>mission</u> set off for the Arctic. A <u>mission</u> is

    Ⓐ   a type of spacecraft.

    Ⓑ   a place built by Spanish priests.

    Ⓒ   a group with an important task to perform.

    Ⓓ   a group of tourists.

20. Kristen's work schedule is left to her <u>discretion</u>. This means that she

    Ⓐ   is trusted to set her own work hours wisely.

    Ⓑ   gets her work schedule from her boss.

    Ⓒ   leaves the work she can't do to an associate.

    Ⓓ   set up a work schedule for an associate.

21. Which of the following is an <u>exaggeration</u>?

    Ⓐ   I'm hungry enough to eat two slices of pizza.

    Ⓑ   Brian knows all there is to know about the moon.

    Ⓒ   Amber is very talented.

    Ⓓ   The company is likely to go bankrupt.

22. Kaitlyn <u>consented</u> to head the team. <u>Consented</u> means

    Ⓐ   refused.

    Ⓑ   preferred.

    Ⓒ   requested.

    Ⓓ   agreed.

23. They have <u>extensive</u> plans to remodel. <u>Extensive</u> means that

    Ⓐ   there will be a lot of changes.

    Ⓑ   the changes will be quite costly.

    Ⓒ   the plans are too extravagant for them.

    Ⓓ   the plans were painstakingly made.

24. Booth and his allies <u>intrigued</u> against Lincoln. <u>Intrigued</u> means

    Ⓐ   led a campaign.

    Ⓑ   plotted.

    Ⓒ   ran for office.

    Ⓓ   spread cruel gossip.

25. The company offers many <u>opportunities</u>. This means that it

    Ⓐ   offers good health insurance.

    Ⓑ   provides many comforts, such as a gym and pool.

    Ⓒ   provides many chances for people to rise in the company.

    Ⓓ   produces a wide range of products.

26. Carmen Miranda wore <u>fantastic</u> hats piled high with fruit. <u>Fantastic</u> means

    Ⓐ   attractive.

    Ⓑ   complicated.

    Ⓒ   hard to believe.

    Ⓓ   gigantic.

27. An <u>engrossing</u> conversation is one that

    Ⓐ   has your complete attention.

    Ⓑ   disgusts you.

    Ⓒ   draws a lot of people.

    Ⓓ   goes on for a long time.

28. To win people's <u>esteem</u>, you should

    Ⓐ   wear expensive clothes.

    Ⓑ   hang out with a popular crowd.

    Ⓒ   be aware of the newest fads.

    Ⓓ   be honorable and trustworthy.

29. Which of these would be considered a <u>marvel</u>?

    Ⓐ   a new light switch

    Ⓑ   the expanse of a great waterfall

    Ⓒ   a napping cat

    Ⓓ   a rescheduled meeting

30. Which is MOST likely to <u>intrigue</u> someone?

    Ⓐ   a film about the mysteries of the pyramids

    Ⓑ   an arrogant remark

    Ⓒ   a domesticated cow

    Ⓓ   a sudden storm

Book 6, Lesson 15 Test

Find a SYNONYM for each underlined word. Then fill in the circle next to your answer.

1. There was a good reason for Corey's <u>apprehension</u>.

   Ⓐ anger
   Ⓑ uneasiness
   Ⓒ terror
   Ⓓ thankfulness

2. They were <u>scaling</u> the mountain when the storm hit.

   Ⓐ mapping
   Ⓑ descending
   Ⓒ measuring
   Ⓓ climbing

3. A mist <u>enveloped</u> the forest.

   Ⓐ shrouded
   Ⓑ battered
   Ⓒ dampened
   Ⓓ exposed

4. The detective <u>analyzed</u> the crime.

   Ⓐ persecuted
   Ⓑ examined
   Ⓒ condemned
   Ⓓ excused

5. Does this chair <u>revolve</u>?

   Ⓐ lower
   Ⓑ adjust
   Ⓒ swivel
   Ⓓ creak

6. The velocity of bullet trains is amazing.

   Ⓐ efficiency
   Ⓑ range
   Ⓒ comfort
   Ⓓ speed

7. The photographers traced the bear to a cave.

   Ⓐ drew
   Ⓑ tracked
   Ⓒ lured
   Ⓓ chased

8. The cruise dates coincide with my scheduled vacation.

   Ⓐ conflict with
   Ⓑ follow
   Ⓒ match
   Ⓓ complicate

Find an ANTONYM for each underlined word. Then fill in the circle next to your answer.

9. The damp soil fused the buried sword to its sheath.

   Ⓐ separated
   Ⓑ melted
   Ⓒ revealed
   Ⓓ hid

10. Michele composed herself before the meeting.

    Ⓐ dirtied
    Ⓑ denounced
    Ⓒ upset
    Ⓓ excused

11. The production was extraordinary.

    Ⓐ brief
    Ⓑ average
    Ⓒ unusual
    Ⓓ inspiring

12. There were <u>traces</u> of mud on the floor.

    Ⓐ   tracks

    Ⓑ   stains

    Ⓒ   reminders

    Ⓓ   clumps

13. The tickets cost a <u>mere</u> three dollars.

    Ⓐ   shocking

    Ⓑ   perpetual

    Ⓒ   vital

    Ⓓ   substantial

Choose the BEST way to complete each sentence or answer each question. Then fill in the circle next to your answer.

14. Which of the following has <u>scales</u>?

    Ⓐ   a flower

    Ⓑ   a snake

    Ⓒ   a mouse

    Ⓓ   a roof

15. The first step in <u>tracing</u> a drawing is to

    Ⓐ   buy a frame for it.

    Ⓑ   put it on a photocopier.

    Ⓒ   put a sheet of lightweight paper over the original.

    Ⓓ   look in every room of the house.

16. Did giants ever <u>exist</u>? The question is:

    Ⓐ   Were giants ever real?

    Ⓑ   Did giants manage to survive?

    Ⓒ   Did giants ever leave records behind them?

    Ⓓ   Were giants able to meet their basic needs?

17. <u>Compose</u> is to song as

    Ⓐ   music is to art.

    Ⓑ   design is to building.

    Ⓒ   listen is to music.

    Ⓓ   sing is to audience.

18. Musical <u>scales</u> are

     Ⓐ   the lines on which musical notes are drawn.

     Ⓑ   short pieces to practice.

     Ⓒ   a series of short tunes.

     Ⓓ   a series of rising or falling notes.

19. An <u>analysis</u> showed that the rock was mostly granite. An <u>analysis</u> is

     Ⓐ   someone who studies stones.

     Ⓑ   a display of precious stones.

     Ⓒ   a process for cutting up stones into useful parts.

     Ⓓ   a careful study of the whole and its parts.

20. What is MOST likely to make someone <u>apprehensive</u>?

     Ⓐ   getting money in the mail

     Ⓑ   using a new shampoo

     Ⓒ   walking past a fierce dog

     Ⓓ   studying for long hours

21. A birthday that <u>coincides</u> with Independence Day is

     Ⓐ   shortly before it.

     Ⓑ   shortly after it.

     Ⓒ   on the same date.

     Ⓓ   in the same month.

22. Which of these is shaped like a <u>disk</u>?

     Ⓐ   a plate

     Ⓑ   a basketball

     Ⓒ   a can of soup

     Ⓓ   a sheet of paper

23. A <u>scale</u> can be used to

     Ⓐ   identify degrees of difference.

     Ⓑ   clean fish.

     Ⓒ   check the temperature of water.

     Ⓓ   record growth.

24. A few broken branches were the only <u>traces</u> of the storm. <u>Traces</u> are

  Ⓐ victims.
  Ⓑ damages.
  Ⓒ warnings.
  Ⓓ signs left behind.

25. Strange fish <u>exist</u> deep in the sea. <u>Exist</u> means

  Ⓐ are caught.
  Ⓑ float.
  Ⓒ can be found.
  Ⓓ hide themselves.

26. What is ice cream usually <u>composed</u> of?

  Ⓐ cream and sugar
  Ⓑ a banana split
  Ⓒ an accompaniment to pie
  Ⓓ grocery stores

27. This model is built on a <u>scale</u> of one inch to one foot. This means that

  Ⓐ if the original is six feet long, the model is six inches long.
  Ⓑ it measures between one inch and one foot.
  Ⓒ it is built on a platform one inch high and one foot square.
  Ⓓ it will be one foot long when completed.

28. What is <u>fusion</u>?

  Ⓐ a mixed-up state of mind
  Ⓑ a state of dissolving
  Ⓒ the combining of matter, often by heating
  Ⓓ separating matter into small parts

29. <u>Solar</u> energy is

  Ⓐ energy from hot water.
  Ⓑ energy from the sun.
  Ⓒ the energy that one person produces.
  Ⓓ energy in the form of hard matter.

30. Which of the following is a <u>coincidence</u>?

    Ⓐ   choosing two flavors of ice cream for your cone

    Ⓑ   seeing your best friend at your birthday party

    Ⓒ   being certain that you can succeed at a task

    Ⓓ   being born on your grandfather's birthday

31. You need warm clothes to <u>exist</u> in the Arctic. <u>Exist</u> means

    Ⓐ   travel.

    Ⓑ   stay alive.

    Ⓒ   explore.

    Ⓓ   visit.

32. A doctor is likely to use <u>scales</u> to

    Ⓐ   check your heartbeat.

    Ⓑ   take a blood sample.

    Ⓒ   check your weight.

    Ⓓ   figure out your bill.

Book 6, Lesson 16 Test

Find a SYNONYM for each underlined word. Then fill in the circle next to your answer.

1. Inside the cave, they were struck with <u>awe</u>.

    Ⓐ terror
    Ⓑ anxiety
    Ⓒ joy
    Ⓓ wonder

2. People's memories often <u>deceive</u> them.

    Ⓐ assist
    Ⓑ trick
    Ⓒ confuse
    Ⓓ rescue

3. We <u>reinforced</u> the posts holding up the dock.

    Ⓐ replaced
    Ⓑ attached
    Ⓒ strengthened
    Ⓓ rotated

4. The sound of rain on the roof <u>lulls</u> me.

    Ⓐ soothes
    Ⓑ disturbs
    Ⓒ interests
    Ⓓ distracts

5. The two runners <u>collided</u>.

    Ⓐ crashed
    Ⓑ competed
    Ⓒ blundered
    Ⓓ tied

6. The steps down the cliff are <u>treacherous</u>.

    Ⓐ   lofty

    Ⓑ   secure

    Ⓒ   dangerous

    Ⓓ   crumbling

Find an ANTONYM for each underlined word. Then fill in the circle next to your answer.

7. We reacted strongly to her <u>stern</u> words.

    Ⓐ   somber

    Ⓑ   kind

    Ⓒ   idle

    Ⓓ   terse

8. We'll just have to <u>improvise</u> our dance.

    Ⓐ   rehearse

    Ⓑ   produce

    Ⓒ   introduce

    Ⓓ   revise

9. Christina had a <u>placid</u> smile on her face.

    Ⓐ   affectionate

    Ⓑ   lofty

    Ⓒ   nervous

    Ⓓ   extraordinary

10. Losing one's job can be a <u>catastrophe</u>.

    Ⓐ   disaster

    Ⓑ   benefit

    Ⓒ   defeat

    Ⓓ   education

11. A <u>treacherous</u> soldier gave away their plan.

    Ⓐ   stingy

    Ⓑ   foolish

    Ⓒ   sinister

    Ⓓ   loyal

Choose the BEST way to complete each sentence or answer each question. Then fill in the circle next to your answer.

12. A typical <u>consequence</u> for breaking a rule is

    Ⓐ   payment.

    Ⓑ   a better grade.

    Ⓒ   punishment.

    Ⓓ   fame and glory.

13. What is a <u>loom</u> used for?

    Ⓐ   to sweep floors

    Ⓑ   to weave fabric

    Ⓒ   to tie up a boat

    Ⓓ   to mislead someone

14. An <u>awesome</u> sight is likely to

    Ⓐ   make you run away.

    Ⓑ   cause you to laugh.

    Ⓒ   fill you with wonder and amazement.

    Ⓓ   make you scornful.

15. The lion's lazy movements are <u>deceptive</u>. They

    Ⓐ   mislead us into thinking it is too sluggish to move.

    Ⓑ   tell us that the lion is about to nap.

    Ⓒ   show how lions usually move.

    Ⓓ   have meaning for other lions.

16. Campers can use garbage bags to <u>improvise</u> rain capes. To <u>improvise</u> is to

    Ⓐ   invent a new product.

    Ⓑ   put something into storage.

    Ⓒ   to pack something into something else.

    Ⓓ   come up with a makeshift solution that will meet your needs.

17. Speeding drivers are responsible for many traffic <u>fatalities</u>. <u>Fatalities</u> are

    Ⓐ   crashes.

    Ⓑ   injuries.

    Ⓒ   traffic fines.

    Ⓓ   deaths.

18. The captain expected <u>reinforcements</u> to arrive by ship. <u>Reinforcements</u> are

    Ⓐ   supplies needed to feed an army.

    Ⓑ   weapons used by an army.

    Ⓒ   extra people sent to provide help.

    Ⓓ   the soldiers of an enemy army.

19. A situation that has <u>priority</u> is

    Ⓐ   one that is difficult to deal with.

    Ⓑ   at the top of a list of things to take care of.

    Ⓒ   something that occurred before anything else did.

    Ⓓ   one that must be kept secret.

20. The error was of no <u>consequence</u>. This means that

    Ⓐ   the error was not an error after all.

    Ⓑ   no one admitted to making the error.

    Ⓒ   no one important had made the error.

    Ⓓ   the error was unimportant.

21. <u>Lull</u> is to storm as

    Ⓐ   pause is to traffic.

    Ⓑ   shadow is to shade.

    Ⓒ   silence is to peace.

    Ⓓ   cloud is to rain.

22. Since the due date <u>loomed</u>, I started my report. <u>Loomed</u> means

    Ⓐ   passed.

    Ⓑ   came frighteningly nearer.

    Ⓒ   was postponed.

    Ⓓ   was set at last.

23. What is MOST likely to <u>awe</u> someone?

    Ⓐ   watching a bad horror movie

    Ⓑ   missing a bus

    Ⓒ   watching a tightrope walker

    Ⓓ   taking a warm bath

24. Where can a <u>stern</u> be found?

  Ⓐ in front of a car

  Ⓑ at a fish market

  Ⓒ in the middle of a boat

  Ⓓ at the rear of a ship

25. Which of the following is a <u>deception</u>?

  Ⓐ claiming that you did a job that you didn't do

  Ⓑ taking a break from writing an essay

  Ⓒ spending long hours on the computer

  Ⓓ forgetting to do an errand

26. <u>Predicament</u> is to solution as

  Ⓐ trouble is to woe.

  Ⓑ leisure is to rest.

  Ⓒ bankrupt is to poor.

  Ⓓ question is to answer.

27. A <u>collision</u> is likely to result when

  Ⓐ two people enter a plot against another.

  Ⓑ someone forgets to fill a car's gas tank.

  Ⓒ two trucks speed toward one another.

  Ⓓ two veteran skaters put on a show.

28. A dark figure that <u>looms</u> out of the fog is most likely to

  Ⓐ seem familiar.

  Ⓑ seem sinister.

  Ⓒ make you smile.

  Ⓓ blunder into you.

Book 6, Lesson 17 Test

Find a SYNONYM for each underlined word. Then fill in the circle next to your answer.

1. The speaker's <u>preliminary</u> remarks captivated us.

   Ⓐ final
   Ⓑ humorous
   Ⓒ opening
   Ⓓ intriguing

2. Katie uses a <u>mobile</u> phone.

   Ⓐ solar
   Ⓑ transportable
   Ⓒ modern
   Ⓓ versatile

3. The beach was covered with <u>debris</u>.

   Ⓐ litter
   Ⓑ seaweed
   Ⓒ driftwood
   Ⓓ pools

4. A film is being made about Powell's <u>exploits</u>.

   Ⓐ discoveries
   Ⓑ expeditions
   Ⓒ adventures
   Ⓓ extravagances

5. Beware of sharp rocks in the <u>ooze</u>.

   Ⓐ slime
   Ⓑ sand
   Ⓒ pond
   Ⓓ weeds

6. Miguel <u>scoured</u> the neighborhood for the cat.

    Ⓐ evacuated
    Ⓑ cleaned
    Ⓒ searched
    Ⓓ walked

Find an ANTONYM for each underlined word. Then fill in the circle next to your answer.

7. The acting in that new sitcom is <u>pathetic</u>.

    Ⓐ terrible
    Ⓑ marvelous
    Ⓒ mediocre
    Ⓓ inept

8. The <u>onset</u> of the illness was gradual.

    Ⓐ convalescence
    Ⓑ duration
    Ⓒ ending
    Ⓓ treatment

9. They constructed a <u>miniature</u> fort.

    Ⓐ colossal
    Ⓑ flimsy
    Ⓒ simple
    Ⓓ crude

10. The news filled Dustin with <u>elation</u>.

    Ⓐ suspense
    Ⓑ jubilation
    Ⓒ optimism
    Ⓓ despair

11. Adrian <u>salvaged</u> the wrecked ship.

    Ⓐ recovered
    Ⓑ claimed
    Ⓒ abandoned
    Ⓓ concealed

12. The rain <u>corroded</u> the metal lawn chairs.

 Ⓐ dirtied

 Ⓑ restored

 Ⓒ battered

 Ⓓ fractured

Choose the BEST way to complete each sentence or answer each question. Then fill in the circle next to your answer.

13. It is against the law to <u>exploit</u> child actors. <u>Exploit</u> means

 Ⓐ publish false information about.

 Ⓑ take advantage of.

 Ⓒ make an agreement with.

 Ⓓ fire from a job.

14. Brooke made a <u>miniature</u> of a birdcage. She made

 Ⓐ an exact copy of the cage.

 Ⓑ a photograph of the cage.

 Ⓒ a improved version of the cage.

 Ⓓ a tiny copy of the cage.

15. <u>Restraints</u> kept the horse from escaping. <u>Restraints</u> refers to

 Ⓐ horse trainers.

 Ⓑ the ropes that controlled the horse.

 Ⓒ people who work on ranches.

 Ⓓ wooden bars in a fence.

16. What could make someone <u>elated</u>?

 Ⓐ having a flat tire

 Ⓑ eating a bowl of cereal

 Ⓒ taking a brief nap

 Ⓓ winning a big prize

17. Leaving for the airport now will give us some <u>leeway</u>. Leaving now will

 Ⓐ get us a lower price on the tickets.

 Ⓑ make it possible to get there more quickly.

 Ⓒ give us some extra time to get there.

 Ⓓ give us more room on the freeway.

18. Where are you most likely to find a <u>mobile</u>?

    Ⓐ   suspended from a museum ceiling

    Ⓑ   stored in a gas station garage

    Ⓒ   arranged on a pedestal

    Ⓓ   parked in a trailer court

19. Their <u>quest</u> took them to the Mountains of the Moon. A <u>quest</u> is

    Ⓐ   a tour guide.

    Ⓑ   a search.

    Ⓒ   a secret message.

    Ⓓ   a map.

20. It was hard to <u>scour</u> the log cabin's floor. To <u>scour</u> is to

    Ⓐ   put something down.

    Ⓑ   make something level.

    Ⓒ   harm something.

    Ⓓ   thoroughly scrub something.

21. It takes <u>restraint</u> not to overact on stage. What is <u>restraint</u>?

    Ⓐ   good training

    Ⓑ   a good imagination

    Ⓒ   self-control

    Ⓓ   an awareness of others

22. Which is likely to leave <u>debris</u> behind?

    Ⓐ   a motorboat

    Ⓑ   a tornado

    Ⓒ   a gentle stream

    Ⓓ   a jet plane

23. Which of the following is a common type of <u>corrosion</u>?

    Ⓐ   rust

    Ⓑ   rips

    Ⓒ   burns

    Ⓓ   scratches

24. Which of the following oozes?

    Ⓐ   dry sand

    Ⓑ   a falling leaf

    Ⓒ   a shower of rain

    Ⓓ   ketchup

25. What is one kind of miniature?

    Ⓐ   a train station

    Ⓑ   a small portrait

    Ⓒ   a diamond

    Ⓓ   a grain of salt

26. Exploit all the features of this software. Exploit means

    Ⓐ   call attention to.

    Ⓑ   analyze.

    Ⓒ   put to use.

    Ⓓ   improve.

27. The wet kitten looked pathetic. This means that it

    Ⓐ   appeared to be hungry.

    Ⓑ   did not look attractive.

    Ⓒ   made us scorn it.

    Ⓓ   aroused our pity.

28. The right of salvage is the right to

    Ⓐ   keep fierce dogs.

    Ⓑ   keep anything rescued from destroyed property.

    Ⓒ   tear down damaged property.

    Ⓓ   make use of your damaged property.

29. Kelly restrained the excited dog. This means that she

    Ⓐ   soothed it.

    Ⓑ   ran after it.

    Ⓒ   held it back and controlled it.

    Ⓓ   trained it to stay calm.

Book 6, Lesson 18 Test

Find a SYNONYM for each underlined word. Then fill in the circle next to your answer.

1. Mark's apology was <u>genuine</u>.

    Ⓐ pathetic
    Ⓑ sincere
    Ⓒ restrained
    Ⓓ grudging

2. A murmur of <u>dissent</u> rose in the room.

    Ⓐ approval
    Ⓑ regret
    Ⓒ disagreement
    Ⓓ sympathy

3. The games <u>commenced</u> at eleven.

    Ⓐ ended
    Ⓑ halted
    Ⓒ paused
    Ⓓ began

4. The boss <u>commended</u> them for their work.

    Ⓐ praised
    Ⓑ criticized
    Ⓒ esteemed
    Ⓓ dismissed

5. Emma <u>hoaxed</u> us all with her story about the snake.

    Ⓐ frightened
    Ⓑ impressed
    Ⓒ fooled
    Ⓓ entertained

6. This wheelchair is easy to <u>manipulate</u>.

    Ⓐ produce
    Ⓑ transport
    Ⓒ assemble
    Ⓓ operate

7. His earnest explanation satisfied his mother.

    Ⓐ detailed

    Ⓑ tearful

    Ⓒ serious

    Ⓓ regretful

Find an ANTONYM for each underlined word. Then fill in the circle next to your answer.

8. The visitors were given a cordial welcome.

    Ⓐ warm

    Ⓑ hostile

    Ⓒ extravagant

    Ⓓ discreet

9. We ended the day in a mood of exhilaration.

    Ⓐ gloom

    Ⓑ satisfaction

    Ⓒ benevolence

    Ⓓ nostalgia

10. My remarks were met with skepticism.

    Ⓐ silence

    Ⓑ support

    Ⓒ hostility

    Ⓓ affection

11. The anguish she felt was beyond description.

    Ⓐ arrogance

    Ⓑ apprehension

    Ⓒ inspiration

    Ⓓ ecstasy

12. Their proposal created controversy.

    Ⓐ confusion

    Ⓑ predicaments

    Ⓒ calm

    Ⓓ restrictions

13. The painting was clearly <u>genuine</u>.

    Ⓐ   inept

    Ⓑ   original

    Ⓒ   fake

    Ⓓ   stolen

Choose the BEST way to complete each sentence or answer each question. Then fill in the circle next to your answer.

14. An <u>exhilarating</u> event is one that

    Ⓐ   stuns you.

    Ⓑ   surprises you.

    Ⓒ   tires you.

    Ⓓ   excites you.

15. A <u>recount</u> may be needed when

    Ⓐ   someone has written a story.

    Ⓑ   votes may have been miscounted.

    Ⓒ   a product is returned to the store.

    Ⓓ   a bill seems wrong.

16. To <u>elicit</u> others' opinions is to

    Ⓐ   draw them out.

    Ⓑ   prohibit them.

    Ⓒ   compare them.

    Ⓓ   pay no attention to them.

17. The orphan was <u>commended</u> to her aunt. <u>Commended</u> means

    Ⓐ   recommended.

    Ⓑ   grateful.

    Ⓒ   given.

    Ⓓ   taken.

18. A trip <u>abroad</u> is one that

    Ⓐ   involves traveling by boat.

    Ⓑ   is taken to another country.

    Ⓒ   is taken to another state.

    Ⓓ   involves traveling by plane.

19. I hadn't expected Shelby to <u>dissent</u>. <u>Dissent</u> means

- Ⓐ   disagree.
- Ⓑ   agree.
- Ⓒ   take part.
- Ⓓ   refuse.

20. Which of the following is a <u>hoax</u>?

- Ⓐ   spending your bus fare on a snack
- Ⓑ   keeping ten dollars that fell from someone's pocket
- Ⓒ   taking the role of a criminal in a play
- Ⓓ   exhibiting a monkey's paintings as a human artist's

21. Vanessa is a <u>skeptic</u> on the subject of flying saucers. This means that she

- Ⓐ   will talk about them for hours.
- Ⓑ   doubts they exist.
- Ⓒ   has created files of data about them.
- Ⓓ   has seen one herself.

22. Jared is helping only because Maria <u>manipulated</u> him. This means that she

- Ⓐ   reasoned with him.
- Ⓑ   ordered him to help.
- Ⓒ   used unfair means to persuade him to help.
- Ⓓ   tracked him down.

23. To <u>anguish</u> over something is to

- Ⓐ   carefully think about it.
- Ⓑ   intensely long for it.
- Ⓒ   apologize for having done it.
- Ⓓ   suffer from doubts about it.

24. <u>Recount</u> is to tale as

- Ⓐ   sing is to song.
- Ⓑ   voter is to election.
- Ⓒ   story is to writer.
- Ⓓ   replay is to play.

25. A <u>controversial</u> issue is one that

     Ⓐ   is important.

     Ⓑ   causes heated debates.

     Ⓒ   will affect the whole community.

     Ⓓ   has the support of the majority.

26. The most <u>exhilarating</u> event of our day was

     Ⓐ   relaxing on the beach.

     Ⓑ   eating hot dogs from a snack bar.

     Ⓒ   surfing on gigantic waves.

     Ⓓ   taking a nap under a beach umbrella.

27. When Luis gave me a <u>skeptical</u> look, I realized that

     Ⓐ   I had upset him somehow.

     Ⓑ   I had my facts all wrong.

     Ⓒ   he wasn't interested in my remarks.

     Ⓓ   he didn't quite believe me.

Book 6, Lesson 19 Test

Find a SYNONYM for each underlined word. Then fill in the circle next to your answer.

1. A <u>massive</u> box blocked the hallway.

   Ⓐ ancient
   Ⓑ abandoned
   Ⓒ substantial
   Ⓓ awkward

2. Jeremy came up with an <u>elaborate</u> plan.

   Ⓐ original
   Ⓑ realistic
   Ⓒ fanciful
   Ⓓ detailed

3. The movie <u>repels</u> all who see it.

   Ⓐ saddens
   Ⓑ disgusts
   Ⓒ contaminates
   Ⓓ inspires

4. The cattle found the <u>breach</u> in the fence.

   Ⓐ wire
   Ⓑ nest
   Ⓒ gap
   Ⓓ food

5. Levi Strauss <u>furnished</u> sturdy pants for gold miners.

   Ⓐ supplied
   Ⓑ invented
   Ⓒ sold
   Ⓓ made

6. They constructed an unusual stage set.

   Ⓐ designed
   Ⓑ painted
   Ⓒ assembled
   Ⓓ imagined

Find an ANTONYM for each underlined word. Then fill in the circle next to your answer.

7. Monica thinks of nothing but retaliation.

   Ⓐ competition
   Ⓑ forgiveness
   Ⓒ victory
   Ⓓ sorrow

8. The construction of the library is going slowly.

   Ⓐ destruction
   Ⓑ abandonment
   Ⓒ conservation
   Ⓓ planning

9. The women strewed flowers along the path.

   Ⓐ tended
   Ⓑ sprinkled
   Ⓒ planted
   Ⓓ gathered

10. The chairperson was installed at the last meeting.

   Ⓐ persecuted
   Ⓑ segregated
   Ⓒ removed
   Ⓓ detained

11. This carpet repels stains.

   Ⓐ inhibits
   Ⓑ absorbs
   Ⓒ conceals
   Ⓓ dissolves

12. A <u>stench</u> filled the back yard.

  Ⓐ silence

  Ⓑ perfume

  Ⓒ dryness

  Ⓓ racket

13. The sheriff <u>restored</u> the Drakes' TV.

  Ⓐ preserved

  Ⓑ purchased

  Ⓒ took

  Ⓓ substituted

14. The company <u>breached</u> its contract with the workers.

  Ⓐ edited

  Ⓑ found

  Ⓒ reinterpreted

  Ⓓ kept

15. That ad is <u>repellent</u>.

  Ⓐ aggravating

  Ⓑ attractive

  Ⓒ drastic

  Ⓓ unoriginal

Choose the BEST way to complete each sentence or answer each question. Then fill in the circle next to your answer.

16. Her bathing suit was <u>clammy</u>. <u>Clammy</u> means

  Ⓐ cold and damp.

  Ⓑ too tight.

  Ⓒ worn out.

  Ⓓ flammable.

17. Which of the following is likely to have a <u>fragrance</u>?

  Ⓐ a computer screen

  Ⓑ a skunk

  Ⓒ hot apple pie

  Ⓓ a flimsy chair

18. This 1862 lighthouse is a <u>restoration</u>. This means that it

    Ⓐ   is a small copy of the original.

    Ⓑ   is an exact copy of the original.

    Ⓒ   was fixed to look as it did originally.

    Ⓓ   is now open for tours.

19. Why might a camper take a <u>repellent</u> along?

    Ⓐ   to stay warm at night

    Ⓑ   to light a fire

    Ⓒ   to use as a raincoat

    Ⓓ   to keep insects away

20. Which are <u>furnishings</u>?

    Ⓐ   garments

    Ⓑ   desks

    Ⓒ   sheds

    Ⓓ   supplements

21. A place that is in your <u>vicinity</u> is

    Ⓐ   one that you often visit.

    Ⓑ   on your usual route.

    Ⓒ   nearby.

    Ⓓ   in your community.

22. What is likely to happen immediately after security is <u>breached</u> in a building?

    Ⓐ   An alarm will go off.

    Ⓑ   Business will continue as usual.

    Ⓒ   Employees will be required to wear hard hats.

    Ⓓ   Visitor passes will be issued.

23. The garden <u>restoration</u> took two years. <u>Restoration</u> is the process of

    Ⓐ   carefully planning a design.

    Ⓑ   making something look as it first did.

    Ⓒ   planting flowers and trees.

    Ⓓ   modernizing the design of a garden.

24. When you <u>elaborate</u> on a plan, you are

   Ⓐ   working with another person.

   Ⓑ   explaining why it won't work.

   Ⓒ   contributing to its success.

   Ⓓ   giving more details about it.

25. The miniature castle is an amazing <u>construction</u>. A <u>construction</u> is

   Ⓐ   a small model of anything.

   Ⓑ   something that has been built.

   Ⓒ   an unusual site.

   Ⓓ   something you enter in a contest.

26. Something that is <u>fragrant</u> appeals to

   Ⓐ   your sense of sight.

   Ⓑ   your sense of taste.

   Ⓒ   your sense of smell.

   Ⓓ   all three of these senses.

27. Copper wire <u>repels</u> garden slugs. The wire

   Ⓐ   lures them.

   Ⓑ   drives them away.

   Ⓒ   gives them shelter.

   Ⓓ   deceives them.

28. To <u>furnish</u> an office, you might

   Ⓐ   go to a real estate office.

   Ⓑ   pay a high rent.

   Ⓒ   have phone lines put in.

   Ⓓ   move in a desk and chair.

29. Her back yard is a <u>haven</u> for birds. <u>Haven</u> means

   Ⓐ   place to eat.

   Ⓑ   nesting ground.

   Ⓒ   sanctuary.

   Ⓓ   cage for captive birds.

30. Batter is to breach as

    Ⓐ   break is to window.

    Ⓑ   rip is to tear.

    Ⓒ   plummet is to stone.

    Ⓓ   woe is to catastrophe.

31. When you install an automobile muffler, you are

    Ⓐ   putting the muffler into the car.

    Ⓑ   comparing prices on mufflers.

    Ⓒ   purchasing a muffler.

    Ⓓ   taking it out of the car.

32. After the attack, the soldiers retaliated by

    Ⓐ   holding up a white flag.

    Ⓑ   sending out a spy.

    Ⓒ   shooting at the enemy.

    Ⓓ   hiding in their camp.

33. Be sure the fabric is water repellent. Look for fabric that

    Ⓐ   sheds water.

    Ⓑ   can be washed.

    Ⓒ   soaks up water.

    Ⓓ   does not shrink when it is wet.

34. After Gabriel restored the table, it looked

    Ⓐ   as it had when it was first made.

    Ⓑ   glossy and new.

    Ⓒ   more up-to-date.

    Ⓓ   as if it had cost a lot more than he paid.

Book 6, Lesson 20 Test

Find a SYNONYM for each underlined word. Then fill in the circle next to your answer.

1. Taking that route was a <u>rash</u> thing to do.

   Ⓐ brave
   Ⓑ foolish
   Ⓒ wise
   Ⓓ intriguing

2. No one <u>dwells</u> in the Old Forest.

   Ⓐ hunts
   Ⓑ lives
   Ⓒ tracks
   Ⓓ lingers

3. The travelers' <u>garments</u> were falling apart.

   Ⓐ tools
   Ⓑ trucks
   Ⓒ maps
   Ⓓ clothing

4. Farmers tried to <u>exterminate</u> the prairie dogs.

   Ⓐ repel
   Ⓑ capture
   Ⓒ boycott
   Ⓓ destroy

5. The prize was <u>paltry</u>.

   Ⓐ genuine
   Ⓑ worthless
   Ⓒ invaluable
   Ⓓ substitute

6. The prince's knights wanted <u>revenge</u>.

    Ⓐ refreshments

    Ⓑ destruction

    Ⓒ retaliation

    Ⓓ restraint

7. Is there a parking <u>fee</u>?

    Ⓐ map

    Ⓑ lot

    Ⓒ space

    Ⓓ charge

8. The salesperson was <u>insistent</u>.

    Ⓐ polite

    Ⓑ pushy

    Ⓒ doubtful

    Ⓓ stubborn

Find an ANTONYM for each underlined word. Then fill in the circle next to your answer.

9. Gabrielle has a <u>peculiar</u> sense of humor.

    Ⓐ placid

    Ⓑ ordinary

    Ⓒ unusual

    Ⓓ superb

10. A <u>blustering</u> storm kept us inside.

    Ⓐ rainy

    Ⓑ perpetual

    Ⓒ gentle

    Ⓓ violent

11. The Vikings' <u>revenge</u> was horrible to watch.

    Ⓐ failure

    Ⓑ skirmish

    Ⓒ terror

    Ⓓ apology

12. The audience <u>swarmed</u> into the auditorium.

   Ⓐ trickled
   Ⓑ stamped
   Ⓒ buzzed
   Ⓓ stampeded

Choose the BEST way to complete each sentence or answer each question. Then fill in the circle next to your answer.

13. Your <u>dwelling</u> is

   Ⓐ your school.
   Ⓑ your neighborhood.
   Ⓒ the structure you live in.
   Ⓓ the town you live in.

14. <u>Rodent</u> food is made for

   Ⓐ dogs and cats.
   Ⓑ pet rats.
   Ⓒ birds of prey.
   Ⓓ tropical fish.

15. A <u>rash</u> of crank calls came in on April first. A <u>rash</u> is

   Ⓐ a lull.
   Ⓑ a pair of occurrences.
   Ⓒ a few occurrences.
   Ⓓ many occurrences.

16. When you <u>insist</u> on something, you are

   Ⓐ making a firm demand.
   Ⓑ giving a thorough description of it.
   Ⓒ explaining why your opinion is correct.
   Ⓓ giving it up for the sake of peace.

17. To <u>dwell</u> on your woes is to

   Ⓐ create more problems for yourself.
   Ⓑ put your troubles behind you.
   Ⓒ refuse to stop thinking about them.
   Ⓓ think of ways to solve your problems.

18. You would be most likely to hear <u>bluster</u> from

    Ⓐ   a weather forecaster.

    Ⓑ   the captain of a boat.

    Ⓒ   a salesclerk.

    Ⓓ   a bully.

19. A <u>council</u> is

    Ⓐ   a public meeting room.

    Ⓑ   an organized group of people with a purpose.

    Ⓒ   a society to do good.

    Ⓓ   the officers of an institution.

20. Which of the following could <u>infest</u> a picnic?

    Ⓐ   wasps

    Ⓑ   close friends

    Ⓒ   outdoor games

    Ⓓ   barbecued chicken

21. <u>Vat</u> is to water as

    Ⓐ   tub is to bath.

    Ⓑ   cup is to glass.

    Ⓒ   sack is to grain.

    Ⓓ   bottle is to air.

22. The baby's <u>rash</u> showed up as

    Ⓐ   a slight temperature.

    Ⓑ   red marks on its skin.

    Ⓒ   fussy behavior.

    Ⓓ   constant crying.

23. That custom is <u>peculiar</u> to the Pawnee. This means that

    Ⓐ   the Pawnee know it is an odd custom.

    Ⓑ   they practice the custom carefully.

    Ⓒ   it is practiced only by them.

    Ⓓ   they are the only people who don't practice the custom.

24. Christine <u>revenged</u> herself on her brother by

    Ⓐ   putting glue in his sneakers.

    Ⓑ   inviting him to the movies.

    Ⓒ   working quietly in her room.

    Ⓓ   going out with her friends.

25. A <u>swarm</u> of locusts settled on the field. The locusts

    Ⓐ   were starving.

    Ⓑ   were making a loud buzzing sound.

    Ⓒ   were killing one another.

    Ⓓ   were traveling in a dense mass.

26. The customer <u>blustered</u> until the manager came out. <u>Blustered</u> means

    Ⓐ   asked for help.

    Ⓑ   was loud and threatening.

    Ⓒ   pled with the sales clerk.

    Ⓓ   waited patiently.

27. A <u>rodent</u> is MOST likely to

    Ⓐ   make a nest in a tree.

    Ⓑ   growl when it sees a stranger.

    Ⓒ   gnaw its way out of a cardboard box.

    Ⓓ   fly from branch to branch.

Read the passage. Choose the BEST answer for each sentence or question about an underlined word. Then fill in the circle next to your answer.

DOWN THE COLORADO RIVER

The Colorado River <u>wends</u> its way through the steep rock walls of the Grand Canyon. Until the middle of the nineteenth century, the river had never been navigated and much of the <u>territory</u> around the canyon was still unmapped. In 1858, Lieutenant Joseph Ives and his party rode along the canyon. They then followed a very steep and dangerous trail down the side of the canyon. It was so frightening that some of the men crawled on their hands and knees. Lieutenant Ives wrote, "It seems by nature that the Colorado River, along the greater portion of its lonely and majestic way, shall be forever unvisited and undisturbed."

In 1869, however, a science professor and Civil War <u>veteran</u> named John Wesley Powell put together an <u>expedition</u> of ten men to explore the canyon by boat. Although he was only 35 years old, Powell had already successfully explored the Rocky Mountains. He also had a knack for getting money to fund his projects and choosing volunteers for the expedition. Except for Powell's brother, all of his recruits were tough and experienced mountain men. Since Powell did not fully realize what a challenge the river would present, he included no boatmen among his crew.

Powell and his men <u>commenced</u> their journey in four boats at Green River Station, Wyoming. They knew that their trip would be a <u>perilous</u> one, for they'd heard stories of deaths on the river and of previous failed expeditions. Although Powell and his crew had tried to <u>anticipate</u> the hardships that lay ahead, they had not fully realized just how <u>treacherous</u> the Colorado River was. Within a month, they had lost one boat and most of their supplies. One man announced that he had experienced "more excitement than a man deserves in a lifetime" and hiked back alone. The rest continued on.

The chief hazard of the river was its many rapids. It was extremely difficult to <u>manipulate</u> a boat through these wild, fast-moving stretches of water without crashing. Whenever possible, the men got past the rapids by towing the boats along the bank or by <u>hauling</u> them over the canyon's narrow, rocky shores. Several of the men came very close to drowning. In addition to the rapids, they had other dangers to face. Once, a whirling wind whipped their campfire into a great blaze, and they were forced to jump into their boats to escape. Some of their supplies were burned in the fire and some were lost when the cook stumbled and dropped their plates, spoons, knives, and forks into the water.

In spite of each day's rigors, the men wrote in their journals at night to record their enjoyment of the <u>marvelous</u> scenery around them. Powell did not forget that the purpose of the journey was to gather information, and he filled his journal with descriptions of the landscape features and wildlife they saw. He did his best to draw a rough map of the region.

Finally, after traveling for three months over 1,000 miles of river, Powell and his crew emerged from the canyon and learned that they had been given up for dead. Having proved that the river could be navigated, Powell made another trip down it in 1871 to gather more scientific data.

1. What does wends mean?

    Ⓐ   cuts

    Ⓑ   travels

    Ⓒ   slips

    Ⓓ   gushes

2. A synonym for territory is

    Ⓐ   desert.

    Ⓑ   wilderness.

    Ⓒ   plains.

    Ⓓ   region.

3. In this story, the word veteran means

    Ⓐ   an experienced person.

    Ⓑ   a person with knowledge of wild areas.

    Ⓒ   a expert sailor.

    Ⓓ   a person who has served in the armed forces during wartime.

4. Powell put together an expedition of ten men. What does expedition mean?

    Ⓐ   a group whose purpose is to meet with heads of state

    Ⓑ   a group whose purpose is to go on a journey of exploration

    Ⓒ   a plan for exploring an unknown area

    Ⓓ   a small group of soldiers

5. What is an antonym for the word commenced?

    Ⓐ   ended

    Ⓑ   started

    Ⓒ   sustained

    Ⓓ   transferred

6. A <u>perilous</u> journey is

    Ⓐ   likely to take a long time.

    Ⓑ   foolish.

    Ⓒ   full of dangers.

    Ⓓ   extensive.

7. In this passage, to <u>anticipate</u> is to

    Ⓐ   foresee and prepare for something.

    Ⓑ   become excited about something.

    Ⓒ   to dread something in the future.

    Ⓓ   to ignore something.

8. In this passage, <u>treacherous</u> refers to

    Ⓐ   the traits of Powell's crew.

    Ⓑ   the boats being used for the expedition.

    Ⓒ   the Grand Canyon's rocky walls.

    Ⓓ   the hidden dangers of the river.

9. The men had to <u>manipulate</u> their boats. <u>Manipulate</u> means

    Ⓐ   carry over rocks.

    Ⓑ   tow.

    Ⓒ   skillfully operate.

    Ⓓ   manufacture.

10. A synonym for <u>hauling</u> is

    Ⓐ   abandoning.

    Ⓑ   carrying.

    Ⓒ   tipping.

    Ⓓ   floating.

11. Which of the following is an example of <u>marvelous</u> scenery?

    Ⓐ   a patch of weeds

    Ⓑ   the boats used by Powell's expedition

    Ⓒ   a campfire

    Ⓓ   snow-capped mountain peaks

12. The men <u>emerged</u> from the canyon. This means that they

    Ⓐ   were worn out by it.

    Ⓑ   sent out messages from it.

    Ⓒ   came out of it.

    Ⓓ   swarmed through it.

Book 6, Final Test 2 (Lessons 1–20)

Read the passage. Choose the BEST answer for each sentence or question about an underlined word. Then fill in the circle next to your answer.

THE REAL TOM AND HUCK

Tom Sawyer is one of Mark Twain's best-loved works, and one of the main reasons for that is that the book's characters Tom Sawyer and Huckleberry Finn seem so realistic. These two <u>unruly</u>, adventurous boys are so true to life that it's hard to believe that they're mere fiction. In fact, they are not entirely fictional, for in a way these characters really did <u>exist</u>. In a small town in Missouri, a boy called Sam Clemens was always getting into mischief with his friends. Many years later, writing under the pen name of Mark Twain, Sam Clemens turned to memories of his boyhood to write his stories. Tom Sawyer is based on young Sam himself, and Huck Finn is based on Sam's best friend Tom Blankenship. In addition, the boys' hometown of Hannibal, Missouri, <u>furnished</u> the setting for Tom Sawyer's home, St. Petersburg.

Tom Blankenship made a great impression on Sam Clemens. Tom was allowed to do anything he wanted, for he had no mother to look after him. He never went to school, and his education consisted of catching and cleaning fish and acquiring other truly useful skills. <u>Restrained</u> by no one, Tom Blankenship was, according to Twain, "the only really independent person—boy or man—in the community, and by <u>consequence</u> he was tranquilly and continuously happy and was envied by all the rest of us." The fact that other boys' parents forbade them to associate with him only reinforced Blankenship's <u>appeal</u>.

Some of the things that Sam and his friends did inspired the adventures in the books. For example, the treasure hunt in *Tom Sawyer* is loosely based on a <u>genuine</u> incident involving Sam, Tom, and another boy. Hannibal's <u>inhabitants</u> had kept alive a legend that a fur trapper had buried treasure in the vicinity and had never dug it up again. One day Tom told Sam and another friend that he had had wonderful dream that had revealed the treasure's location. He said that if they would help him dig for it, he would share it with them. It was a blazing hot summer day, but Sam and the friend dug for hours. Tom sat under a shady tree as their <u>sentinel</u>. At the end of the day, the two diggers decided that they had not dug deep enough. They returned to dig a second day, and by the end of the afternoon Sam and the friend <u>griped</u> that it was time to quit. That night, however, Tom dreamed that the treasure was somewhere else. Hearing his dream, the other two put in a third day of digging in the hot sun. Then, thoroughly <u>exhausted</u>, Sam and the other boy announced that they were giving up the search for good. Tom was forced to give up on the treasure, too, but he <u>insisted</u> that the problem was with their digging—not with his dreams. It was proof of Tom's influence over the other boys that they never questioned the truth of his dreams or his unwillingness to use a shovel himself.

1. <u>Unruly</u> boys are ones who

   Ⓐ lived in times past.

   Ⓑ need hair cuts.

   Ⓒ are boisterous.

   Ⓓ are fanciful.

2. In this story, to <u>exist</u> is to

   Ⓐ be real.

   Ⓑ occur somewhere.

   Ⓒ manage to stay alive.

   Ⓓ be a character in a book.

3. Hannibal <u>furnished</u> the book's setting. <u>Furnished</u> means

   Ⓐ provided.

   Ⓑ contributed furniture to.

   Ⓒ described.

   Ⓓ outlined.

4. Tom was <u>restrained</u> by no one. This means that he

   Ⓐ never had any useful training.

   Ⓑ was under no one's control.

   Ⓒ wasn't afraid of anyone.

   Ⓓ he wasn't approved of by anyone.

5. In the second paragraph, the words "by <u>consequence</u>" mean

   Ⓐ more importantly.

   Ⓑ in spite of that.

   Ⓒ as a result.

   Ⓓ without a doubt.

6. To say that Tom Blankenship has <u>appeal</u> means that

   Ⓐ he wants to be friends with everyone.

   Ⓑ many people find him interesting.

   Ⓒ he is very brave.

   Ⓓ he is rich.

7. A <u>genuine</u> incident is one that

    Ⓐ   is sincere.

    Ⓑ   is different from a later version.

    Ⓒ   is realistic.

    Ⓓ   really took place.

8. Hannibal's <u>inhabitants</u> were

    Ⓐ   the people visiting there.

    Ⓑ   the people dwelling there.

    Ⓒ   the people living nearby.

    Ⓓ   the people who had been there the longest.

9. Acting as <u>sentinel</u>, Tom

    Ⓐ   relaxed and dozed.

    Ⓑ   gave the other boys orders.

    Ⓒ   guarded the digging site.

    Ⓓ   made all the plans.

10. As it is used in this story, <u>griped</u> means

    Ⓐ   complained.

    Ⓑ   annoyed.

    Ⓒ   announced.

    Ⓓ   voted.

11. The <u>exhausted</u> boys were

    Ⓐ   in a bad mood.

    Ⓑ   out of patience.

    Ⓒ   losing faith.

    Ⓓ   tired out.

12. Tom <u>insisted</u> that the problem lay in the digging. <u>Insisted</u> means

    Ⓐ   suggested.

    Ⓑ   firmly declared.

    Ⓒ   mumbled.

    Ⓓ   whined.

Book 6, Final Test 3 (Lessons 1–20)

Read the passage. Choose the BEST answer for each sentence or question about an underlined word. Then fill in the circle next to your answer.

THE WAR OF THE WORLDS

One of the greatest <u>hoaxes</u> of all time was not intended to be one. The American public was misled by its own failure to question <u>fantastic</u> and impossible "facts."

In 1938, radios provided entertainment the way that television does today. Music, news, comedy, adventure tales, and serious drama attracted a wide circle of listeners. Drama fans often enjoyed a show that featured plays by the <u>prominent</u> actor and director Orson Welles. On October 30, Welles and his cast put on an <u>adaptation</u> of a famous novel called *War of the Worlds*, in which Martians land on earth. To make the play more exciting for radio listeners, Welles rewrote it to sound like a news broadcast.

Welles's <u>preliminary</u> remarks made it clear that the audience was about to hear a play. Listeners then heard dance music, as they would during an ordinary radio show. During the music, an actor broke in and <u>declared</u> that a space ship had landed. As the show continued, other actors pretended to be reporters or government officials watching the Martians take over the United States. They provided <u>elaborate</u> descriptions of the horrors that emerged from the space ship. One newscaster cried, "Something's wriggling out of the shadow like a gray snake. Now it's another one, and another. They look like tentacles to me. There, I can see the thing's body. It's large as a bear and it glistens like wet leather. But that face. It...it's indescribable. I can hardly force myself to keep looking at it." Background sounds and the actors' frightened voices made it sound as if a real <u>catastrophe</u> was taking place.

Welles's aim had been to fascinate his audience, not terrify it. He never imagined the <u>effect</u> that the program would have on some of the people who tuned in late. It never occurred to him that anyone could think such an impossible event could be true. Some people, however, believed anything they were told, and were convinced that the Martians were real. They never questioned the likelihood of such an <u>extraordinary</u> event. They never even thought to check its truth by tuning in to other radio stations. Instead, they panicked. Believing their lives were in <u>jeopardy</u>, some people hid in cellars or other places that seemed safe. Many loaded up their cars and tried to flee to the countryside, creating traffic jams on the roads leading out of cities.

The program caused a lot of controversy. People who had been fooled were not ashamed of themselves but angry with Welles. They demanded that the government take <u>drastic</u> measures, such as prohibiting programs of that kind to be broadcast. Other people felt that the program taught a valuable lesson. According to one writer, "Mr. Orson Welles and the Mercury Theater of the Air have made one of the most fascinating and important demonstrations of all time. They have proved that a few effective voices, accompanied by sound effects, can convince masses of people of a totally unreasonable, completely fantastic proposition as to create a nation-wide panic." The same writer predicted it would become easy to use mass communications to manipulate the public's thoughts and actions.

1. Hoaxes are

    Ⓐ radio plays.

    Ⓑ mistakes that confuse people.

    Ⓒ acts intended to fool people.

    Ⓓ unfortunate errors.

2. In the first paragraph, fantastic means

    Ⓐ interesting.

    Ⓑ marvelous

    Ⓒ hard to believe.

    Ⓓ odd.

3. A prominent actor is one who

    Ⓐ is well known.

    Ⓑ is easy to see.

    Ⓒ stands out in a landscape.

    Ⓓ is very talented.

4. Orson Welles's adaptation was

    Ⓐ a plan to convince people that Martians are real.

    Ⓑ a play that was developed from a novel.

    Ⓒ a plan for using radios in a more useful way.

    Ⓓ a scheme to attract a wider audience.

5. Preliminary remarks are remarks

    Ⓐ made to soothe people.

    Ⓑ that explain what is happening.

    Ⓒ made before a main program.

    Ⓓ that explain a musical number.

6. A synonym for declared is

    Ⓐ worried.

    Ⓑ dissented.

    Ⓒ questioned.

    Ⓓ stated.

7. What is an <u>elaborate</u> description?

    Ⓐ   one that describes a splendid sight

    Ⓑ   one that is full of details

    Ⓒ   one that is difficult to follow

    Ⓓ   one that is very terse

8. Another word for <u>catastrophe</u> is

    Ⓐ   invasion

    Ⓑ   expedition

    Ⓒ   disaster

    Ⓓ   arrival

9. An <u>effect</u> is something that

    Ⓐ   is a result of something else.

    Ⓑ   frightens people.

    Ⓒ   causes people to make mistakes.

    Ⓓ   tricks people.

10. An antonym for <u>extraordinary</u> is

    Ⓐ   peculiar.

    Ⓑ   superb.

    Ⓒ   disturbing.

    Ⓓ   common.

11. People felt they were in <u>jeopardy</u>. <u>Jeopardy</u> is

    Ⓐ   a state of panic.

    Ⓑ   the condition of being uninformed.

    Ⓒ   great danger.

    Ⓓ   a need for reassurance.

12. What is a <u>drastic</u> measure?

    Ⓐ   a stern act

    Ⓑ   an extreme action

    Ⓒ   a legal action

    Ⓓ   a practical solution

Book 6, Final Test 4 (Lessons 1–20)

Read the passage. Choose the BEST answer for each sentence or question about an underlined word. Then fill in the circle next to your answer.

CAPTAINS COURAGEOUS

The writer Rudyard Kipling was impressed by the <u>hardy</u> men who fished the Grand Bank in the North Atlantic Ocean. His admiration led to his writing *Captains Courageous*, an adventure novel set on a fishing boat. It was first published in 1897 and has remained in print ever since.

The main character, Harvey Cheyne, is the spoiled, <u>arrogant</u> son of an incredibly rich man. His father ignores him and his mother spoils him. When the story opens, twelve-year-old Harvey is on an ocean liner traveling from New York to Europe. He swaggers into the lounge and tries to impress the gentlemen relaxing there. Instead, they dislike and pity him. One later remarks that he can see good in Harvey, but that someone needs to bring it out. Harvey shows off by accepting a strong cigar from one of the men, but the cigar makes him sick. He staggers out of the lounge to the ship's rail. There he is <u>enveloped</u> by a wave that washes him overboard.

When he comes to his senses, Harvey finds himself lying on a pile of fish in a small rowboat. He had been dragged out of the water in someone's fishing <u>haul</u>. Taken to the main fishing boat, Harvey announces that his father will pay well if the captain immediately returns him to New York. Captain Troop dismisses the boy's remarks about his father's wealth as <u>fanciful</u>, no doubt the result of a head injury when he was swept overboard. He informs Harvey that they are 1,000 miles from New York and that they are certainly not going to turn back. If they did so, they would lose most of their profits from the fishing season—an amount of money far greater than the <u>paltry</u> reward that could be expected from Harvey's father.

Harvey realizes that he has no choice but to <u>accompany</u> the crew and work with them for the next four months. Making the best of his situation, he turns into a <u>diligent</u> worker and begins to win the respect of the others on board. He also makes his first really close friend, the captain's son Dan, a boy of his own age. With Dan as his example, Harvey takes on his tasks without protesting. He discovers the satisfaction of going to bed <u>fatigued</u> after putting in a good day's work. As the months pass, Harvey is <u>elated</u> to realize that he is liked and accepted by the crew. He recognizes that his <u>contributions</u> have played their part in making their fishing trip a success.

By the time the boat returns home, Harvey feels like the older and wiser brother of his earlier self. He quietly gets word to his father that he is alive, and his parents quickly come to get him in their private railroad car. Captain Troop is stunned to find out that Harvey's tales about his family are true. When Harvey and his father talk, his father <u>appreciates</u> Harvey's changes for the better. For the first time, father and son respect one another and begin to plan a future for Harvey that will someday become a partnership between them.

1. An antonym for <u>hardy</u> is

    Ⓐ   feeble.

    Ⓑ   stubborn.

    Ⓒ   strong.

    Ⓓ   apprehensive.

2. An <u>arrogant</u> person is

    Ⓐ   full of opinions.

    Ⓑ   prejudiced.

    Ⓒ   proud in a rude way.

    Ⓓ   of no consequence.

3. When Harvey is <u>enveloped</u> by the wave, he is

    Ⓐ   knocked over by it.

    Ⓑ   sprayed by it.

    Ⓒ   splashed by it.

    Ⓓ   covered by it.

4. In this story, <u>haul</u> describes

    Ⓐ   the amount caught at one time in a fishing net.

    Ⓑ   a long distance.

    Ⓒ   the act of pulling something.

    Ⓓ   a boat used for fishing.

5. In the third paragraph, <u>fanciful</u> means

    Ⓐ   honest.

    Ⓑ   blustering.

    Ⓒ   untrue.

    Ⓓ   marvelous.

6. A <u>paltry</u> reward is

    Ⓐ   generous.

    Ⓑ   quite small.

    Ⓒ   slow to appear.

    Ⓓ   grudging.

7. In this story, <u>accompany</u> means

  Ⓐ work with.

  Ⓑ get to know someone.

  Ⓒ go along with.

  Ⓓ surrender to someone.

8. As a <u>diligent</u> worker, Harvey

  Ⓐ was very lively and active.

  Ⓑ put care and effort into what he did.

  Ⓒ learned quickly.

  Ⓓ was cheerful.

9. A synonym for <u>fatigued</u> is

  Ⓐ filthy.

  Ⓑ early.

  Ⓒ exhausted.

  Ⓓ silent.

10. How does an <u>elated</u> person feel?

  Ⓐ surprised by a new thought

  Ⓑ placid and satisfied

  Ⓒ a little apprehensive

  Ⓓ happy and excited

11. What was Harvey's <u>contribution</u>?

  Ⓐ the effort he put into the group's work

  Ⓑ the encouragement he felt

  Ⓒ a large sum of money

  Ⓓ useful advice

12. In this story, <u>appreciates</u> means

  Ⓐ can't quite believe.

  Ⓑ is overpowered by.

  Ⓒ sees the worth of.

  Ⓓ increases in value.

Answer Key

Lesson 1 Test

1. A
2. B
3. D
4. B
5. D
6. C
7. D
8. B
9. C
10. D
11. B
12. A
13. D
14. C
15. B
16. B
17. C
18. D
19. A
20. C
21. C
22. D
23. B
24. C
25. D
26. B
27. A
28. C
29. D
30. A
31. B
32. D
33. C

Lesson 2 Test

1. B
2. C
3. A
4. B
5. B
6. D
7. C
8. A
9. B
10. D
11. C
12. D
13. C
14. A
15. A
16. C
17. B
18. D
19. C
20. B
21. C
22. C
23. D
24. C
25. B
26. B
27. A
28. D
29. B
30. C
31. D
32. A
33. C

Answer Key

Lesson 3 Test

1. B
2. A
3. D
4. D
5. C
6. B
7. B
8. A
9. C
10. B
11. D
12. A
13. B
14. D
15. C
16. B
17. A
18. D
19. B
20. C
21. C
22. D
23. B
24. A

Lesson 4 Test

1. B
2. D
3. D
4. B
5. C
6. B
7. A
8. A
9. C
10. C
11. D
12. C
13. B
14. A
15. C
16. D
17. C
18. C
19. A
20. C
21. B
22. D
23. C
24. B
25. A

Answer Key

Lesson 5 Test

1. C
2. D
3. A
4. B
5. C
6. A
7. C
8. B
9. D
10. C
11. D
12. B
13. C
14. A
15. D
16. A
17. B
18. C
19. D
20. B
21. A
22. C
23. B
24. C
25. D

Lesson 6 Test

1. C
2. B
3. A
4. C
5. D
6. D
7. B
8. C
9. D
10. B
11. A
12. C
13. D
14. B
15. C
16. D
17. A
18. C
19. B
20. A
21. C
22. B
23. A
24. D
25. D
26. C
27. B
28. A
29. C
30. D
31. B
32. C
33. D
34. A

Answer Key

<table>
<tr><td>Lesson 7 Test</td><td>Lesson 8 Test</td></tr>
<tr><td>1. C</td><td>1. C</td></tr>
<tr><td>2. B</td><td>2. A</td></tr>
<tr><td>3. A</td><td>3. D</td></tr>
<tr><td>4. D</td><td>4. C</td></tr>
<tr><td>5. D</td><td>5. B</td></tr>
<tr><td>6. B</td><td>6. D</td></tr>
<tr><td>7. C</td><td>7. B</td></tr>
<tr><td>8. A</td><td>8. C</td></tr>
<tr><td>9. D</td><td>9. D</td></tr>
<tr><td>10. B</td><td>10. A</td></tr>
<tr><td>11. B</td><td>11. B</td></tr>
<tr><td>12. C</td><td>12. C</td></tr>
<tr><td>13. D</td><td>13. A</td></tr>
<tr><td>14. A</td><td>14. C</td></tr>
<tr><td>15. C</td><td>15. D</td></tr>
<tr><td>16. D</td><td>16. A</td></tr>
<tr><td>17. B</td><td>17. B</td></tr>
<tr><td>18. C</td><td>18. C</td></tr>
<tr><td>19. C</td><td>19. D</td></tr>
<tr><td>20. D</td><td>20. C</td></tr>
<tr><td>21. B</td><td>21. B</td></tr>
<tr><td>22. A</td><td>22. A</td></tr>
<tr><td>23. C</td><td>23. B</td></tr>
<tr><td>24. C</td><td>24. D</td></tr>
<tr><td>25. D</td><td>25. A</td></tr>
<tr><td>26. B</td><td>26. C</td></tr>
<tr><td>27. C</td><td>27. D</td></tr>
<tr><td>28. A</td><td>28. B</td></tr>
<tr><td>29. B</td><td></td></tr>
<tr><td>30. B</td><td></td></tr>
<tr><td>31. D</td><td></td></tr>
<tr><td>32. A</td><td></td></tr>
</table>

Answer Key

Lesson 9 Test		Lesson 10 Test	
1.	C	1.	B
2.	B	2.	C
3.	A	3.	D
4.	D	4.	D
5.	B	5.	C
6.	C	6.	B
7.	D	7.	B
8.	A	8.	D
9.	B	9.	C
10.	D	10.	A
11.	C	11.	C
12.	D	12.	D
13.	A	13.	B
14.	B	14.	A
15.	C	15.	C
16.	A	16.	D
17.	B	17.	B
18.	A	18.	A
19.	C	19.	D
20.	C	20.	C
21.	B	21.	B
22.	C	22.	C
23.	C	23.	D
24.	D	24.	A
25.	B	25.	C
26.	A	26.	D
27.	B	27.	A
28.	C	28.	A
29.	D	29.	B
30.	C	30.	C
31.	B	31.	D
		32.	A
		33.	C
		34.	D
		35.	B

Answer Key

Midterm Test 1
(Lessons 1–10)

1. A
2. C
3. D
4. B
5. B
6. C
7. D
8. B
9. D
10. A
11. C
12. B

Midterm Test 2
(Lessons 1–10)

1. D
2. C
3. B
4. A
5. D
6. C
7. A
8. B
9. C
10. A
11. D
12. B

Lesson 11 Test

1. A
2. D
3. C
4. B
5. C
6. D
7. B
8. A
9. C
10. B
11. C
12. D
13. A
14. B
15. B
16. C
17. C
18. D
19. B
20. A
21. C
22. D
23. B
24. C
25. D
26. B
27. B
28. A
29. D
30. A
31. C

Answer Key

Lesson 12 Test
1. C
2. D
3. B
4. C
5. B
6. A
7. C
8. D
9. D
10. B
11. C
12. A
13. C
14. A
15. B
16. C
17. D
18. B
19. A
20. C
21. C
22. A
23. D
24. B
25. C

Lesson 13 Test
1. B
2. C
3. D
4. C
5. B
6. A
7. B
8. D
9. C
10. B
11. A
12. D
13. B
14. C
15. D
16. C
17. D
18. B
19. A
20. D
21. D
22. B
23. D
24. C
25. D
26. D
27. B
28. C
29. D
30. B
31. C
32. C
33. A

Answer Key

Lesson 14 Test

1. B
2. C
3. A
4. C
5. D
6. B
7. A
8. C
9. D
10. B
11. A
12. C
13. D
14. B
15. B
16. B
17. C
18. B
19. C
20. A
21. B
22. D
23. A
24. B
25. C
26. C
27. A
28. D
29. B
30. A

Lesson 15 Test

1. B
2. D
3. A
4. B
5. C
6. D
7. B
8. C
9. A
10. C
11. B
12. D
13. D
14. B
15. C
16. A
17. B
18. D
19. D
20. C
21. C
22. A
23. A
24. D
25. C
26. A
27. A
28. C
29. B
30. D
31. B
32. C

Answer Key

Lesson 16 Test

1. D
2. B
3. C
4. A
5. A
6. C
7. B
8. A
9. C
10. B
11. D
12. C
13. B
14. C
15. A
16. D
17. D
18. C
19. B
20. D
21. A
22. B
23. C
24. D
25. A
26. D
27. C
28. B

Lesson 17 Test

1. C
2. B
3. A
4. C
5. A
6. C
7. B
8. C
9. A
10. D
11. C
12. B
13. B
14. D
15. B
16. D
17. C
18. A
19. B
20. D
21. C
22. B
23. A
24. D
25. B
26. C
27. D
28. B
29. C

Answer Key

Lesson 18 Test

1. B
2. C
3. D
4. A
5. C
6. D
7. C
8. B
9. A
10. B
11. D
12. C
13. C
14. D
15. B
16. A
17. C
18. B
19. A
20. D
21. B
22. C
23. D
24. A
25. B
26. C
27. D

Lesson 19 Test

1. C
2. D
3. B
4. C
5. A
6. C
7. B
8. A
9. D
10. C
11. B
12. B
13. C
14. D
15. B
16. A
17. C
18. C
19. D
20. B
21. C
22. A
23. B
24. D
25. B
26. C
27. B
28. D
29. C
30. B
31. A
32. C
33. A
34. A

Answer Key

Lesson 20 Test

1. B
2. B
3. D
4. D
5. B
6. C
7. D
8. B
9. B
10. C
11. D
12. A
13. C
14. B
15. D
16. A
17. C
18. D
19. B
20. A
21. C
22. B
23. C
24. A
25. D
26. B
27. C

Final Test 1
(Lessons 1–20)

1. B
2. D
3. D
4. B
5. A
6. C
7. A
8. D
9. C
10. B
11. D
12. C

Answer Key

Final Test 2
(Lessons 1–20)

1. C
2. A
3. A
4. B
5. C
6. B
7. D
8. B
9. C
10. A
11. D
12. B

Final Test 3
(Lessons 1–20)

1. C
2. C
3. A
4. B
5. C
6. D
7. B
8. C
9. A
10. D
11. C
12. B

Final Test 4
(Lessons 1–20)

1. A
2. C
3. D
4. A
5. C
6. B
7. C
8. B
9. C
10. D
11. A
12. C